A PUBLIC HEALT

COMBATING INSTITUTIONAL RACISM THROUGH MENTORING

NATASHA A. PATTERSON, PHD, MPH

FOREWORD BY DR. CRYSTAL LUCKY

COMBATING INSTITUTIONAL RACISM THROUGH MENTORING: A PUBLIC HEALTH APPROACH

Natasha A. Patterson, PhD, MPH

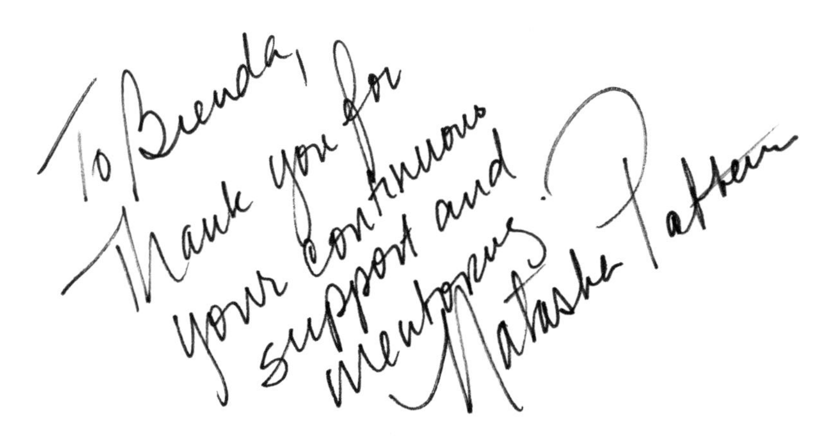

Published by Sims Publishing Group, LLC Washington, DC 20003
www.simspublishinggroup.com

Library of Congress Cataloging-in-Publication Data

Combating Institutional Racism Through Mentoring: A Public Health Approach
Patterson, Natasha A.
p. cm

ISBN 978-1-939774-62-0 (pbk. :alk. Paper)
African American students. 2. African American socialization. 3. Educational equalization 4. Academic attainment

Printed in the United States of America

"We need to use our voices...speak up about what we want and need, because our silence doesn't serve anyone. Being quiet about our lives, stories, problems, and lessons does us no favors. When we want to say something and our voice shakes, we should take that to spur us forward, because that is when it is most necessary. Let your voice tremble but say it anyway."

-Luvvie Ajayi Jones

Dedication

To all of the students and faculty who are the ONLY and the FIRST to blaze the trail — your sacrifice is not in vain.

To the mentors who give of themselves — your time, efforts, and support provided to students will have a long-lasting impact on them and the field.

Acknowledgements

To God be the glory! I received constant encouragement, support, love, and accommodations from my village that includes my family: mom, Teresa C. Hinton; husband, Brett Patterson; children: Khari, Kiara, and Kamari and a wonderful friend group; support and guidance from my editor and colleague, Dr. Natasha Pollard. Dr. Crystal Lucky and Rev. Dr. Lorina Marshall Blake for their contributions; my friends and mentors: Brenda Seals, Angela Beale Tawfeeq, and my former students and mentees, especially Salomine Ekambi, Diana Washington and Eva Doughan. My sisters in the National Coalition of 100 Black Women-PA Chapter, the National Association of University Women, and the La Mott AME Women's Prayer group are all wonderful supporters and encouragers.

Table of Contents

Foreword

The study of 19th and 20th century African American literature and culture might appear to have little scholarly overlap with the field of public health. However, as a professor of the literature and lived experiences of Black people, a university administrator who regularly interacts with students from underrepresented communities, and the pastor of a predominantly Black church, I have both an intimate connection with and vested interest in the questions raised by Combating Institutional Racism through Mentoring: A Public Health Approach.

Research abounds documenting the ways chronic diseases like diabetes, heart disease, high blood pressure, and obesity disproportionately affect Black communities. Alarming statistics highlight the reality that Black maternal morbidity and mortality rates in the United States are two to three times higher than that of Whites. According to the Center for Disease Control (CDC), "Black/African American people account for a higher proportion of new HIV diagnoses and people with HIV, compared to other races and ethnicities." The COVID pandemic not only uncovered ever widening health disparities among Black people in comparison with Whites and other ethnic populations in the United States; it revealed the dearth of accessible mental health resources within those communities. If we have learned anything, it is the importance of healthcare workers and public health professionals who identify as

Black or African American who minister to the physical and psychological wounds resulting from the unethical and duplicitous medical research practices performed on Black people in the not-too-distant past. The necessary presence of Black doctors, nurses, public health professionals, and support personnel remains essential to raise levels of trust among Black people about the best public health practices needed to effect significant and positive change. And yet, the numbers of Black public health professionals remain small.

Research shows that at both the undergraduate and graduate levels, students are empowered by the support of academic professionals, both inside and outside of the classroom, who share aspects of their identity, whether race, ethnicity, gender, gender expression, language, or class. So, while the research demonstrates the need to improve academic and training opportunities for developing public health professionals, those opportunities likely extend outside relationships with discipline-specific practitioners. Professors of not only the social sciences, but the natural sciences and liberal arts, along with administrators within their respective colleges have an important part to play in the support and development of underrepresented students interested in public health as a profession. Dr. Patterson rightly argues that "effective mentorship has had a significant impact on the success of these students and their ability to overcome the roadblocks created by systemic racism as they attempt to move through the pipeline to public health leaders and decision makers."

Implicit in Combating Institutional Racism through Mentoring is the acknowledgement that models of mentorship are many. Moreover, mentoring responsibilities should not fall on the shoulders of just one, powerful individual whose advice must be followed to the letter. Instead, the most effective mentoring is characterized by distributive and collaborative exchanges among an ever-expanding group of professionals and supportive individuals who offer their time, wisdom, formal recommendations, experiential learning opportunities, evaluative feedback, listening ears, and welcoming spaces to individuals throughout the course of their academic and professional careers. An effective mentoring network for underrepresented students and developing professionals in public health should be composed of people from their undergraduate colleges and universities, graduate programs, living communities, and families. In other words, the mentoring process is multi-layered, nuanced, and organic.

Dr. Patterson is equally correct in highlighting the cumulative effect of institutional racism on the production of public health officials of color. This phenomenon, in turn, affects the hiring, retention, and promotion of faculty of color in all disciplines at most institutions of higher education. Many students who understand the need to connect with, learn from, and gain the professional and personal support of faculty of color rely heavily on those faculty members who are already likely the only or one of a few Black faculty in their departments. As they are confronting their own challenges conducting meaningful research, publishing in top-tier journals and with reputable presses, and teaching in predominantly White classrooms, they also carry the load of disproportionate levels of service responsibilities, often related to issues of diversity, equity, inclusion, and anti-racism within their respective departments, colleges, and universities. Thus, Combating Institutional Racism through Mentoring implicitly calls for further research and action with respect to recruiting, hiring, retaining, awarding tenure to, and promoting faculty of color who can support students of color seeking to obtain terminal degrees. The process ultimately contributes to the creation of a pipeline not only for producing students prepared to enter public health fields but also positioning faculty of color to assume administrative leadership roles within their institutions.

Artists, intellectuals, researchers, teachers, and practitioners continue to engage in the ever-circling debate about the relevance of and connection between one's social identity and one's work. Some dismiss concerns about the scarcity of faculty of color in higher education classrooms as mere identity politics fueled by essentialist thinking. But for the real students who come from real communities affected by dire economic, health, housing, and environmental disparities and inequities, envisioning a path forward for themselves, their families, and their communities begins not only with education. Many have heard and absorbed the mantra that "knowledge is power." They are committed to taking the first step. What they need after the power of knowledge are the strategies for surviving isolation (being the first, the only, the best, the unique) in the very classrooms that promise such power. These future professionals need shelter from the insensitivity of educators who have never met the very people about whom they care the most and desperately wish to serve. And they need access to the experiential learning opportunities that often evolve through mentoring relationships and networks that then lead to further professional prospects. Dr. Patterson's important work offers insight into the best path forward for preparing the next generation of Black public health professionals who will engage with dignity the underserved communities so often left behind.

—Dr. Crystal J. Lucky

Associate Dean of Baccalaureate Studies,

CLAS and Professor of English at Villanova University

Preface

When first asked to write the preface for "Combating Institutional Racism Through Mentoring: A Public Health Approach" by Dr. Natasha Patterson, I was both flattered and humbled. However, when I sat down to write the preface, a flood of emotions came over me, as I pondered just where to begin. From what perspective or vantage point could or should I approach such a daunting subject? Most individuals that know me in Philadelphia are aware that I wear many hats, both literally and figuratively. And, my dilemma and challenge would be exactly what "hat" would I wear in addressing this most important topic. Would I wear my professional healthcare "hat" of 30 years? Would I wear my ministerial 'hat" of 25 years? Would I wear my community innovator "hat" of over 40 years? Would I wear my 30 year "hat" as a member of Alpha Kappa Alpha Sorority, Inc? But most importantly, no matter what "hat" I selected just how is it applicable to our subject matter, "Combating Institutional Racism Through Mentoring: A Public Health Approach." I concluded that I would attempt to use all of these "hats" in addressing this pressing statement which was begging for some answers. I believe we can all agree that there is an elephant in the room and for decades it has taken up residence in this city, this state, this nation. Institutional racism has been around for a very long time. And, it has been overlooked by too many, for far too long – whether by willful ignorance, benign neglect, or inhumane indifference. And it continues, whether we are addressing Health, Education, Housing, Law and Policing. And yes, Mentoring.

The Macpherson Report calls out Institutional Racism as "the collective failure of an organization to provide an appropriate and professional service to people because of their color, culture, or ethnic origin." It can be seen or detected in processes, attitudes, and behaviors which amount to discrimination through unwitting prejudice, ignorance, thoughtlessness and racist stereotyping which disadvantages minority ethnic people. Simply stated "you don't matter." Unfortunately, during my professional career, there were not many mentors who looked like me, who could be my advocate or sponsor. But this instilled in me a commitment to stand in the gap and pry open the door for advancement for my people who weren't asking for a handout, just a hand. Yes, can you help a brother or sister out with their career trajectory? Quite frankly, it is in my DNA. In Jeremiah 29:11, God tells Jeremiah, "For the Lord declares I have a plan for your life, not to harm you, but to prosper you and to give you hope and a future." You see mentoring goes all the way back to the Bible. And, it was God's approach for "all" people. Oddly enough, this too could be called a public health approach. This institutional racism can be traced all the way back to the beginning of time. Thus, it is not a new battle. But we have to be better prepared for combat, forearmed with strategies that will benefit all. In essence, as you succeed, I succeed. All boats rise together. We all have to make a commitment to our fellow journeymen and women to share our wisdom on how to successfully navigate the narrative and culture of the environments in which we find ourselves.

I believe Dr. Patterson's approach and The Public Health approach practiced in many circles requires that we 1) define the problem; 2) identify the risk and protective factors; 3) develop and test prevention strategy; and 4) assure widespread adoption. I end this preface with a "hats off" to Dr. Patterson for writing such a thought-provoking and insightful approach to addressing the enigma of "institutional racism." And, I leave with a quote on mentoring from Tony Dungy, Former Head Coach, Tampa Bay Buccaneers and Indianapolis Colts: *"Building a life of significance and creating a legacy of real value means being willing to step out in life and onto the platforms of influence you've been given and touch the lives of people in need whether it's in your business, your school, your community or your family. If you want to "make a difference" in the lives of the people you lead, you must be willing to walk alongside them to lift and encourage them to share moments of understanding with them, not just shout down at them from on high. Mentors build mentors. Leaders build leaders. When you look at it closely, it's really one and the same."*

—Rev. Dr. Lorina Marshall-Blake
President of the Independence
Blue Cross Foundation and Vice President,
Community Affairs, Independence Blue Cross

Introduction

The purpose of this book is not only to highlight the experiences of students, but to identify the ways in which having a well-trained and culturally competent mentor can be a protective factor in reducing or preventing the negative effects of institutional racism. The ideal solution is to dismantle current systems and rebuild anew with inclusion and care at the core.

However, history has shown that there is an unwillingness to take what may be perceived as drastic action. Harmful practices and policies are ingrained in our academic institutions to the point where they are norms. It will take time and effort for systemic change to take place. In the meantime, we must utilize the tools we have available to us to support students and faculty. Hence the title of this book: *Combating Institutional Racism through Mentoring: A Public Health Approach* is appropriate in that we are, as the definition states, "striving to reduce or eliminate the effects of institutional racism" (Merriam-Webster, 2022). Institutional racism has a long history, just like redlining, forced migration, and economic segregation. The American Public Health Association declared racism a Public Health Crisis in 2020 (Benjamin, 2020). The Center for Disease Control and Prevention declared racism a serious threat to the public's health in 2020 (CDC, 2020).

Most educational institutions in the United States were created with exclusion in mind. Historically, academic institutions were created only for a specific subgroup of the population: White, Christian males. All policies, procedures, and practices were developed and implemented with that subgroup in mind. "Higher education began as a privileged institution, designed to advance a certain kind of student and exclude others" (Carlton, 2020). Over time, everyone else had to fight to be allowed into these institutions. New laws and policies had to be created or addendums made to current policies and practices. Despite new and revised policies, taking on this fight came at the risk of being continually harmed and marginalized. In order to take a public health approach to addressing this problem, mentoring can be used as the intervention strategy to facilitate socialization, knowledge transfer, and capacity building (Sambunjak, 2015; Thomas, Willis & Davis, 2007). Public Health is about prevention and doing what is possible to prevent future harm. In evidence based public health practice, the following framework is used (Figure 1).

As outlined in the diagram, the first step is to assess the problem and quantify the issue. This can be done by measuring student success outcomes, faculty-student engagement activities, identifying stress factors, and student perceptions of their experiences. The assessment data provides a picture of the problem. This leads to the next step in "developing a concrete statement of the issue" (Yost et al, 2014, p. 2). Once the problem is clearly defined, it is time to search the literature for what is known about the problem, successes, challenges, theories, and frameworks used to study the problem. The literature will also provide recommendations for solutions or next steps. There are various methods and strategies that could be implemented to address the problem. Using this framework to inform decisions when developing effective programs and policies (Yost et al, 2014).

Figure 1. Evidence-Based Public Health Framework

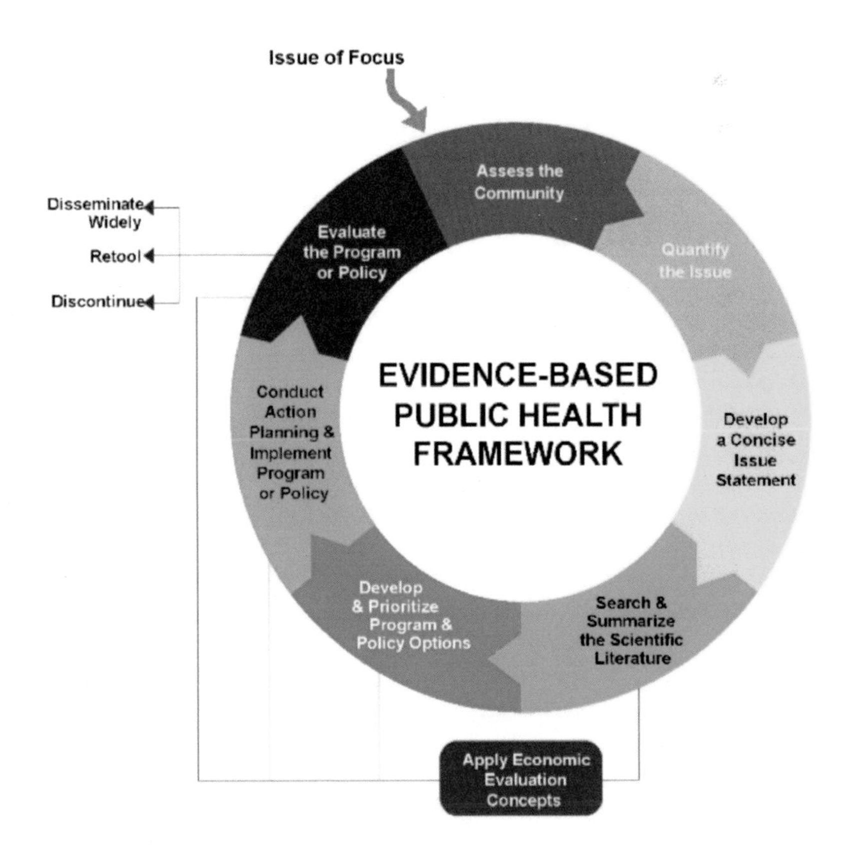

For the purpose of this book, effective and inclusive mentoring is the desired behavior, therefore behavior change theories can be used to develop interventions. There are theories and frameworks like the Transtheoretical Model for Change that allows for progression through stages in order to reach the ultimate goal. Considering that it takes time, training, modeling, and practice to become an effective mentor, some space is needed to make mistakes or revert back to former practices. This is allowed within the Transtheoretical Model for Change (Figure 2). This model has been used in research focused on faculty resistant to online teaching (Mitchell, Parlamis, & Claiborne, 2015). This model can be used for faculty who may be resistant to change when it comes to how they provide mentoring to students or those who may be resistant to providing mentorship at all (Behar-Horenstein & Zhang, 2018).

The Ecological Model supports the idea of using a holistic approach to addressing a problem. There are levels and activities associated with each level (see Figure 3). This allows for a more comprehensive intervention strategy; college campuses have opportunities for change at every level. Institutions can make changes at the same time that faculty and staff can make the changes they need to make. "An ecological model of mentoring is proposed that takes into account various factors broadly operating at different contextual levels" (Sambunjak, 2015, p. 47).

Figure 2. Transtheoretical Model for Change

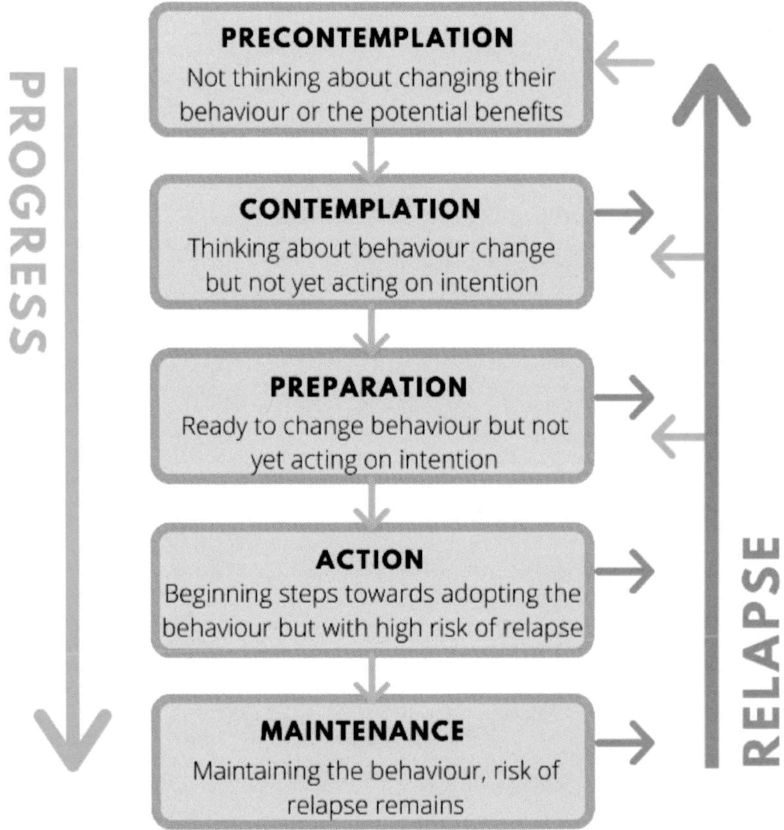

Figure 3. Ecological Model

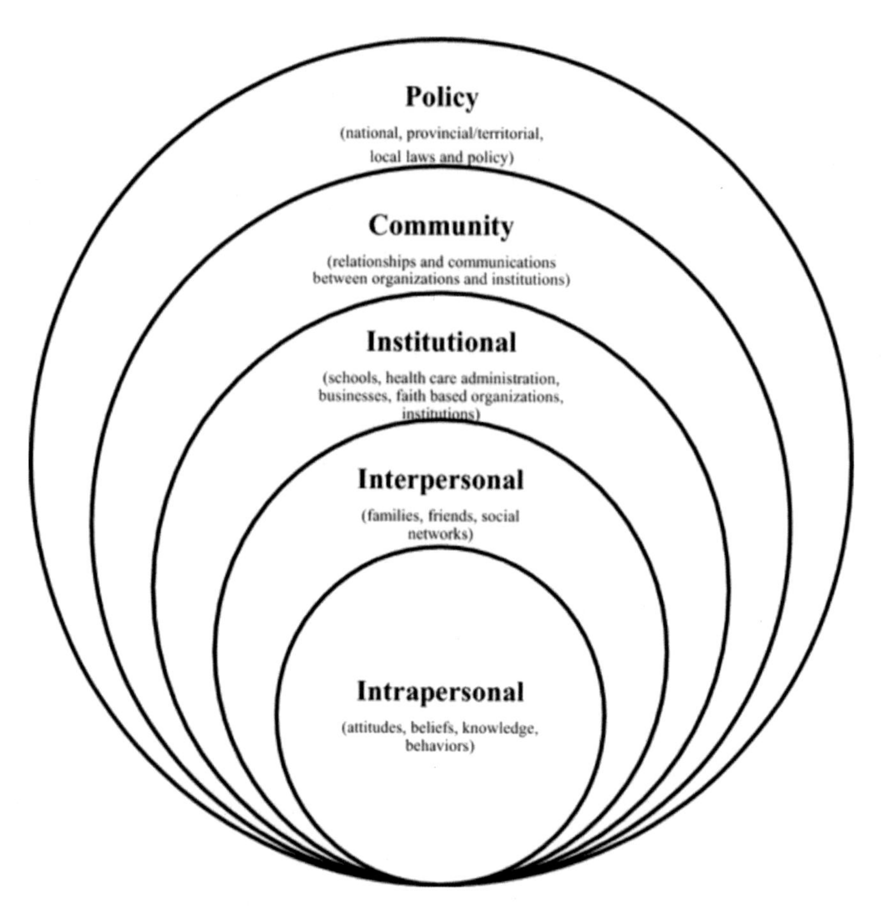

In this book, the historical context will be provided as well as the outcomes, and the potential solutions for addressing institutional racism. There is evidence that demonstrates that there are strategies that have been used to mitigate harms due to institutional racism. Mentoring is one of them and is the focus of this book.

Introduction

Faculty-student engagement takes many forms. Faculty serve as instructors, advisors, research supervisors, mentors and more. The faculty-student mentoring relationship is valuable and unique, contributing to the doctoral process; therefore, it is important to understand how students from diverse groups perceive the efficacy of the relationship. The literature on mentoring includes explorations into the faculty-student mentoring experiences of Black doctoral students (Barker, 2011; Felder & Barker, 2013; Gasman et al., 2008; Sethna, 2011). Barker (2011), Felder and Barker (2013), and Gasman et al. (2008) specifically examined the experiences of Black doctoral students in predominantly White institutions (PWI).

There are many resources developed to support Black students in PWIs (Felder, 2010; Heather, 2020; Stanton et al., 2022). There are books, conferences, and support groups specifically for Black doctoral students, providing tips and strategies for navigating not only the doctoral process but the institutional challenges they may face as Black students. The same goes for Black faculty and academic leaders. There is a phrase, *Black in the Ivory*, now a hashtag and a movement, started by Dr. Sharde' M. Davis to provide a space of Black academics to share their stories about racism in academia and provide resources and support. Black faculty, students and staff in higher education are constantly looking for ways to navigate around a system that was not built with them in mind. It has been past the time for those in positions of power to acknowledge and address these issues and make the changes necessary to dismantle these systems.

If you are a higher education leader, you have an opportunity to use this book as a guide that will provide the language and strategies to help use your position and authority in a way that will benefit all students, faculty, and staff. Creating safe spaces of belonging for your most marginalized groups will have a positive impact on all who take part in it. Review your institutions policies and practices. This includes codes of conduct, curriculum, syllabi, admissions and hiring practices. Interview your faculty, staff, and students; find out how these policies and practices are impacting them, and if and how, they are creating barriers to success and/or causing harm. Do so in a way that does not do further harm; provide a safe space for them to share their perspective without any threat of retaliation for what they might *share. Check the lens through which you see your faculty, staff, and students. Some self-work may need to be done. Check your biases and assumptions. This process may feel uncomfortable but push through anyhow.*

If you are faculty reading this book, thank you. You may also use this as a guide. I encourage you to take a look at your own teaching philosophy and pedagogical practices. *Check the lens through which you see your students and your colleagues. Check your biases and assumptions. It may feel uncomfortable but push through anyhow.* Think about how these practices impact your day-to-day interactions with your students and colleagues. This book is written for the purpose of raising awareness and sharing the stories of students and faculty with respect to their mentoring experiences.

For students and faculty, who have been marginalized, this is validation for you, this is the proof you need that you are not imagining things. You may be the "only" or one of few in your program, department, or institution, but you are not alone in your experience.

This book highlights the challenges PhD programs have with recruitment, retention, and completion when it comes to Black students and the impact this has on a field that is continually focused on eliminating health disparities. These challenges stem from institutional racism: the structures that hinder Black students in their quest for higher learning. These barriers in the form of policy and practice have been in place for centuries. Because it is structural — often built into the system, it permeates throughout all levels of the academy. Structural barriers in place at the undergraduate level impact the rates of Black students who go on to pursue graduate study, consequently or simultaneously impacting the pipeline to public health leadership and the professorate. This in turn impacts the pipeline to public health leadership positions and the professoriate.

Chronic diseases like diabetes and heart disease disproportionately impact Black communities. The Black maternal morbidity and mortality rate in the US is more than two to three times higher than Whites and even higher in states like Georgia,

Indiana, New Jersey, and Louisiana. The recent decision to overturn Roe v. Wade disproportionately impacts the Black and Hispanic communities. Leaving the decision up to each state to legalize abortion enhances the inequalities and limited access to quality health care (Artiga et al., 2022). As more states legalize cannabis for recreational and medical use, Black people are still negatively impacted by the criminal practices stemming from the War on Drugs. Black communities have been left ravaged and generations of families destroyed, but many are now financially benefiting from the legalization of cannabis (Bester & Milan, 2022). About 80-90% of cannabis businesses are owned by White people. Since the beginning of the COVID-19 pandemic, Black people have been at increased risk for transmission, hospitalization, and death, but because of the historical medical maltreatment of Black people, there is great mistrust in the COVID-19 vaccine among members of the Black community (Oliove & Vestal, 2020).

For many Black doctoral students, "giving back to their community" via their research is a deciding factor in selecting a topic for their dissertation (McCallum, 2017). They need the support of faculty and their institutions to move their research agenda forward. Currently, institutions report fewer Black faculty who are in tenured positions and able to supervise dissertation research and even fewer Black students in doctoral programs. In 2018 five percent of tenured faculty were Black (NCES, 2019). This percentage is even smaller when we focus on Black tenured faculty at Schools and Programs of Public Health. While there is no guarantee that Black doctoral students will choose to conduct research focused on public health issues plaguing the Black community, the field continues to suffer from lack of representation, input and perspective on health matters pertaining to the Black community.

Addressing public health issues in the Black community is Social Justice work at multiple levels. Health equity continues to be a priority. Black public health leaders and faculty are fighting within the ongoing systemic racism plaguing institutions and organizations while at the same time fighting for students to have the support needed as they navigate these systems while also having to fight for marginalized communities to have access to quality healthcare. It is exhausting.

CHAPTER 1

Student Experiences

Student Case Examples

Each student comes with their own story—their own life experiences that lead them to pursue a career in public health or healthcare. Khayla's story is the perfect example. Khayla's mother is Black and her father was Puerto Rican. Her father passed away before she was born, so she was raised by her mother as a Black girl with no exposure to her father's family and their Puerto Rican heritage. Her mother worked in the healthcare field as an office manager in a physician's office within a children's hospital. The children's hospital was located in a low-income, predominantly Black and Hispanic neighborhood. The physician's specialty was immunology. This was in the early 1980s so many of the young patients coming into the office were diagnosed with HIV or AIDS. Many were born to mothers who were HIV positive.

Khayla's mother became very familiar with the families who came into the office. Since they came in for regular appointments so often, she was able to build a relationship with them, learning their names and their life stories over time. She would often share about her experiences with her young patients with Khalya. At that time, those patients who were diagnosed with HIV at birth did not live past the age of five years old (Alburto, Kristensen, & Sharp, 2021).

It seemed like she was going to funerals all of the time and she would share how heartbreaking it was to see the tiny caskets. Khayla would go to work with her mother sometimes and she gravitated towards the social worker who worked in the same office with her mother. She witnessed the social worker engaging with the patients and noticed how helpful she was to them.

At a very young age, maybe eight years old, Khayla learned about how HIV and AIDS affected people and families. She learned about Ryan White, one of the first children diagnosed with HIV in 1984. Ryan contracted HIV from a blood transfusion. As a young child he fought against AIDS related discrimination. There is legislation named after him: Ryan White Comprehensive AIDS Resources Emergency (CARE) Act (Buchanan & Hatcher, 2007). She also learned about Hydeia Broadbent, who was born in 1984, abandoned at the hospital, adopted, and diagnosed with HIV at three years old. Hydeia became an activist at age six and she is still living and continuing HIV/AIDS work at age 37. These children were very close to Khayla's age and this experience helped to shape her views on health, healthcare and what she would later know as public health.

Tara, a young Black girl, at age 14, had early interests in healthcare. She was advised to volunteer in a hospital as a candy striper to gain some experience. She volunteered at a well-known hospital near her home. This hospital was located in a low-income, predominantly Black community. Her volunteer assignment was in the Neonatal Intensive Care Unit (NICU). She worked closely with the nurses, mostly running errands, and answering phones. Eventually she would be allowed to hold the tiny babies. There was a rocking chair in the room. Tara sat in the chair so the nurse could place the infants in her arms gently, and oftentimes, they were hooked up to cords and tubes. She later noticed that some of the infants did not have visitors. The nurses shared stories of how the babies were born to mothers with addiction to crack cocaine and left the hospital never to return. The babies would cry and cry, and it was difficult to soothe them. The nurses also shared that the babies may have been born addicted to the drugs and were going through withdrawal. Sometimes a social worker would come to check on the babies. Eventually when the babies gained more weight and their strength, they would go into foster care.

As a mentor, it's important to learn about the early experiences of those whom you provide mentorship. Learn about what experiences shape their understanding. Be sure to take the opportunity to learn about the early experiences, even as early as elementary school.

Felicia is a second-year college student, pre-nursing major. The college she attends requires a certain number of courses to be completed, a competitive GPA, and an interview before being admitted to the nursing program. Felicia had a work-study job at the college's hospital affiliate. She worked in the pulmonary (lung) department. She worked closely with the nurses and physicians, but even closer with the office administrative assistants. She learned quickly how much work they do, and without them, the office would be in chaos. They were the backbone of that office and nothing got done without them, and if it did, it wasn't done efficiently or effectively. They were on top of everything, they prepared the physicians for their speaking engagements, they built relationships with the patients, and learned about their lives and their families. They helped the physicians in building those relationships as well. There were four or five physicians in the practice— all of whom were White men— and each physician had an administrative assistant— all of whom were Black women.

Felicia also witnessed the nurses and their efforts. She was surprised how the nurses were treated by the physicians. They were often taken for granted and seemed to be unheard. She witnessed their frustration. This experience gave her additional insight into the career she was pursuing.

Eventually, Felicia finished her prerequisite courses in preparation for applying to the nursing program. She also learned that she was pregnant in September and her due date was in April.

She gave birth to a beautiful baby boy. She was a mom by the time she formally applied to the nursing program. When she met with the director of the nursing program, the first thing she said to Felicia, before mentioning anything about the program and its expectations was, "If you have a boyfriend, get rid of him. You will not have time for that." Felicia never shared with her that she was a new mom. The director never asked any questions to get to know her. Once she finished interviewing with the director, she walked out of the office and went straight to her advisor to change her major. She was already in the process of weighing the pros and cons of continuing on this path. Her experiences at the work study job, her interactions in the classes with other students who also had the goal of wanting to be nurses, and that interview with the director led her to the decision that nursing was not for her. She also visited and interviewed for other nursing programs, thinking maybe it was just this program, but finally Felicia came to the same conclusion. Nursing was not for her.

What assumptions do you make about students before having conversations with them? How do you think those assumptions create barriers to your teaching, advising, and mentoring? Do you try to get to know your students as human beings with experiences, personal interests, and challenges?

James, a recent college graduate, started his first full time, salaried job, working as a case manager providing social services to "adolescent boys at risk for delinquency." He worked for a nonprofit organization. This position exposed him to information about social determinants of health, health disparities, inequities, poverty, and systemic racism. Some of the children he had on his caseload had parents who were battling addiction, suffering from mental illness, enduring domestic violence, experiencing physical health issues, and most were living in poverty. The challenges James faced in trying to assist them were unbelievable as many of the challenges stemmed from policies, including health insurance policies, welfare policies, and disability laws. James began thinking about how complex it is addressing health issues in communities that have been marginalized. It was frustrating and heartbreaking. After 18 months of doing this work, James began to suffer from burnout. He spent so much time and energy trying to do more than he had the resources to do for these families. He was conducting home visits and knew many members of his clients' families. The trauma these children and their parents experienced was a constant barrier to reaching their goals. He only had six months to work with each family. This was an unrealistic timeline compared to the effort and resources that were required to reach their goals.

He eventually found a new position working as a Senior Health Educator. He no longer worked one-on-one with people, but now more in group settings. He no longer conducted home visits, for much of his work was conducted in schools, recreational centers, and hospitals. They used a peer educator model, meaning some of the health educators were from the communities they served. The peers knew the community, its residents, and had great insight into how to meet their needs. James worked with one of the peer educators to do seminars, presentations, and workshops for community members. The topics covered included: asthma management, nutrition, and sexual health, to name a few. He used all that he had learned as a case manager to tailor his health education tools to meet the needs of the community he was serving. James took pride in serving those who lived in the areas of the city with a high poverty rate.

While doing health education and health promotion activities, James met so many others in the field. He always found ways to collaborate and partner for activities. In doing so, he learned about the field of public health. His colleagues had master's degrees in this field and, James wanted to go to graduate school but had yet to figure out his direction. Pursuing a public health degree began to make sense. So, he started investigating programs in the area. In reviewing the course requirements, he realized that the courses perfectly aligned with his work. Many of the programs were full time. He also applied for teaching and research assistant positions to help pay for the program, but because he was working full time, he did not get accepted for those opportunities. He had to take out loans to complete the MPH program.

The first semester he took only two courses to see if he could do it while working full time. His advisor planned out his schedule assuming he would take two classes at a time throughout the program, which would mean that it would take him four years to complete the degree. After completing the first semester taking two courses, he realized that he could handle three courses, which is considered a full-time course load for graduate school. He asked his advisor about changing his course plan from part time to full time. The advisor was totally against it. She said that with him working full time and going to school full time, it would be next to impossible. He left her office feeling frustrated. He felt like he was being treated like a child and his assessment of his own abilities were not considered. He was an adult who was capable of making informed decisions. So, he stopped going to the advisor, reviewed the academic bulletin, and registered for those classes based on the course outline and finished the program in two years. His job was flexible; he was able to leave early on the days he had class. He was also able to complete his homework during downtime at work.

He was promoted to Program Coordinator a few months before graduating with his MPH degree. It was an eye-opening experience and he was able to utilize much of what he learned in his coursework in this new position. However, he later learned from one of his classmates that he could have applied to the PhD program instead of the MPH program and would have gotten the MPH along the way. He wishes he knew that before he started the process. He remembered having PhD students in some of his classes but did not think about why they were there. There was so much information he did not have while navigating through the graduate school process.

He was the first in his immediate family to go this far in college. It would have been helpful to have more information about academic and career opportunities. He did not know about the opportunities available working with faculty on research projects, publications, presenting at conferences, grants, or scholarships. He was encouraged to publish his master's thesis, but he did not even know where to begin. He also did not know how important publications would be to his career. Much of what he needed to know, he had to seek it out or learn from other students who already knew somehow. He soon realized that there were questions that he did not even know to ask.

As a mentor, how have you been able to ensure that students know all of the opportunities available to them? How do you ensure that students understand certain processes that will help them advance? Many times, mentors answer questions that students ask, but what if the student does not know what questions to ask?

The K-12 and Higher Education Connection

Academic advising is a key role in the educational experience of all students, starting with guidance counselors at the K-12 level, to undergraduate advisors, and with faculty graduate advisors, who are becoming even more significant at the higher education level. At each level, students spend more and more time with advisors. Guidance counselors in high school play a key role in students' choices, about their post high school plans, whether it be work, armed forces, tech school or college (2-year or 4-year). Although teachers can influence students' decisions, the role of guidance counselors should truly guide students in areas of academics, course selection, and post high school planning. In undergraduate programs, advisors can play a similar role providing support and guidance for students navigating their course selection process, internships, post-secondary school plans and career decisions. Additionally, graduate program advisors play a critical role, and it is important for faculty and students to truly know the power of mentorship— as mentorship is like a bridge that builds memories, and saves and changes students' lives, and it is via this lens that one must strive to be the best mentor and advisor to all students that they encounter.

The Role of High School Guidance Counselors

High school guidance counselors play a valuable role in a student's academic career and transition after high school (ASCA,

2019). In the case of a high school student, named Nyema, the guidance counselors were assigned to students based on the first letter of their last names. The guidance counselor assigned to Nyema was an older White man. Students were encouraged to meet with their guidance counselor at least one time per year to select courses for the next school year. When Nyema met with her guidance counselor, it was always brief. Nyema was on track with her studies, so she didn't have many questions for him, until the end of her 10th grade year, after taking the PSAT. She started the conversation about colleges. He made a suggestion to her, that maybe she would like to "do hair." She was confused by his suggestion because he did not know her well enough to know her goals or what she might like to do as a career. As previously mentioned, their meetings were brief. He never asked her questions to get to know her. He made an assumption that was incorrect. Now Nyema's hairstyle was always different and she enjoyed expressing her culture and creativity by wearing different hairstyles and clothes, as she was of mixed race. To her, how she styled her hair had absolutely nothing to do with her academic and career goals and he didn't know her enough to know that, but she did not correct him. She just left his office with no intention of having the discussion with him again.

This case speaks to the forced self-reliance that many Black students, specifically Black girls, face when in the process of post-secondary planning (Mayes et al, 2021). It also reflects the notion that guidance counselors are not interested in seeing these students "grow as people" (p. 149). Drake and Oglesby's (2020) research describe the way that schools and guidance counselors "dehumanize or fail to see Black youth, including Black girls" (p.20.)

In Nyema's 11th grade year, a new guidance counselor was hired, a Black woman. All of the Black students were talking about her and were excited for her arrival. At that time, there were no Black guidance counselors employed at this school, and there was only one Black teacher employed there, and this teacher taught an elective course. Nyema went to the new counselor's office to introduce herself. The new guidance counselor greeted Nyema with a smile, Nyema noticed that she had braces and a short haircut, and she spoke with kindness in her eyes. She wore nice suits and blazers. It was obvious to Nyema that she was in a member of a Black Greek sorority because of the décor in her office and she often wore her sorority colors or paraphernalia. She would later tell Nyema that she would love to talk to her about it, if she ever decided to pursue membership of her sorority. At their first meeting, Nyema shared that she wanted her to be her guidance counselor. She said that she couldn't officially be her guidance counselor, but she would help her with whatever she needed. They worked together on identifying colleges for Nyema based on her interests. The guidance counselor helped Nyema obtain fee waivers for the applications. Nyema didn't even know that there was such a thing. Fee waivers were for students who could not afford to pay for SAT exams and college application fees. It could get pretty expensive when applying to multiple schools.

One of the schools Nyema applied to had a $50 application fee. The guidance counselor also helped Nyema think about topics for the essays and goal statements required for the application. She helped Nyema identify and apply for scholarships. For this student, the guidance counselor provided the information and support necessary for the student to progress to the next stage of her academic career. It also speaks to the need for more diversity in the hiring of guidance counselors, because many times as the only Black guidance counselor meeting with students who were not officially on their case load could cause burnout for this guidance counselor. This scenario is not uncommon, only Black teachers, only Black administrators face the same challenges (Jones, 2019).

The Role of College Advisors

College can be a different story. For Malik, an undergraduate student at a large university, the turnover rate for academic advisors was so high, he had a different one every time it was time to select courses for the following semester. Sometimes the course plans changed. Some classes that were required were no longer requirements and vice versa. The academic advisors could hardly keep up with the changes. Depending on who he went to, they told him something different. He and his classmates became frustrated with this experience. This was the time before online processes, so they had to stand in line and wait in a waiting room every time it was time to see the advisor. He eventually stopped going and decided to just pay close attention to the academic bulletin when selecting his courses. He changed his major twice. He first wanted to do social work, then nursing. The second time, he changed it from nursing to sociology. Later when in graduate school at the same university, his advising experience was similar. He again eventually stopped going in for advising meetings. However, this time he did find a professor who eventually became more of a mentor to him. That continued after graduation into his career. How do faculty advisors help students transition when they don't have solid, consistent mentors throughout their academic career?

Mentoring is not the same for all students. As these brief case studies show, just because you are an advisor does not automatically make you a mentor. Mentorship takes skill and practice. Academic advisors need training and so do mentors. This training should include education about the experiences and issues their students are facing (Thomas, Willis, & Davis, 2007). From an equity standpoint, it is important to meet students where they are, understand their goals and their challenges, and listen to them. Applying the same format to every student in the same way will leave some students left out. Pay attention to the language you use, including your body language. "There are parts of our brain that are very, very sensitive to nonverbal relational cues" (Perry & Winfrey, 2021, p. 33).

Making assumptions about students, their backgrounds, their families, and their resources will hinder the relationship between the student and the advisor. It also limits your ability to be a resource for them. When hiring for these positions, think of not only the job duties but also the empathy that is needed. Students will have challenges and need to come to an advisor for assistance. When they seek assistance, what are they faced with? Who is greeting them? Will that person meet them with understanding and empathy? Advisors not only assist students with academics, they also connect them to resources, such as the office of disabilities, financial aid, or the recovery programs on campus. Students come to advisors with various needs also. Those needs may not seem to be academic in nature but have everything to do with their academic success.

Students also have varied experiences in the classroom. Black students experience racism in the classroom. They have to be able to share this with someone who can help. Trauma-informed advising allows for active listening, mental health awareness, and active inclusion. It's also strength-based, identifying the student's abilities and building on them (Doughty, 2020).

In higher education, there is much talk about access. There are so many resources on campus. Many times, higher education leaders are curious as to why students are not taking advantage of the resources available to them. I remember attending a talk by Dr. Beronda Montgomery, a botanist. She wrote a book called "Lessons from Plants." In her talk she used the analogy, comparing plants to students. She said when a plant does not thrive, we look at the environment, the amount of sunlight it's exposed to, the water, etc. We don't blame the plant.

However, when a student is not thriving in an institution, we look at the student, the ownness is on the student to take steps to improve somehow. She went on to say that we could place a plant next to a water source and say it has access to water. Just like placing resources on campus and saying students have access to them. We have to be purposeful about how we are going to get the resources to the students. In public health, people have access to hospitals, food sources, and health information but unless we have a purposeful way to connect them to those resources, we cannot say they truly have access. We have to do better.

CHAPTER 2

Institutional Racism and Promoting Equity in Higher Education

History

Institutional racism is defined as, "a system in which public policies, institutional practices, cultural representations, and other norms work in various, often reinforcing ways to perpetuate racial group inequity" (The Aspen Institute). Institutional or structural racism permeates the practices, policies, and culture of the entire institution. So, anyone who works within the system can carry out these policies and practices knowingly or unknowingly. It's important to highlight this information because it sets the foundation for the challenges and barriers we face today in higher education and eventually in the public health field. Higher education institutions were built with the Christian White male in mind. The policies and practices were developed for this very specific demographic. Knowing this will help us to understand the challenges and barriers that arise once we start to include those whom we would identify as "other."

Historically, colleges and universities were founded out of churches and Christian beliefs.

The first settlers believed that God had specific instructions for living and one of them was to pursue education (Lucas 2006). The mission of these colleges was based on Christian doctrine. When Harvard University was first founded, its mission was "Everyone shall consider the main end of his life and studies to know God and Jesus Christ, which is eternal life…and therefore to lay Christ in the bottom as the only foundation of all sound knowledge and learning" (p. 104). Those in training to be religious leaders attended colleges like this studying scripture and Christian doctrine. As time progressed throughout the 18th century, the separation of church and state began to challenge the religious foundation of the colleges. As government funded land grants and other resources became available, many of these colleges and universities rooted in the Christian faith revised their vision and mission to be more inclusive and secular. However, not all schools made this change, many were able to maintain their religious foundation while providing quality education.

Secularization theorists believe that with modernization of US culture, religious institutions of higher education will decline. Religious colleges and universities will have to revise their missions and visions to be more inclusive and secular. Global growth is demonstrated in an article by Glanzer, Carpenter and Lantinga (2011) stating that "Contrary to the assumptions of secularization theory, the narrative of Christian higher education is not one of linear decline" (p. 735). It is important to demonstrate the strength and significance of Christian education despite what is happening with secular institutions.

Due to the growth of institutions during this period, college governance and organizational structure formed what would become current day institutional governance structures. The Dartmouth College Case said, "help lay the foundations for the legal distinction between a 'public' and 'private' college" (Lucas, 1994, p. 114). As stated above, private colleges were started out of religious doctrine and did not seek funds from legislation. In having funds from private sources, they were able to preserve their traditions. They would not have to adhere to policies put forth by the legislation since they were not funded by it. Public colleges had to adhere to the policies and procedures set forth by the legislation. Today it is similar in that private colleges use private funds and reserve the right to have their own policies and procedures.

The governance structure of institutions started out as the board of trustees, the president, faculty and tutors. The Board of Trustees or governing boards were advisors who voted on policies and procedures. These individuals were non-academics and prominent members of the community. "There were not enough scholars to form a self-governing body, but a group of laypeople could organize an institution and employ a president to manage it (Cohen and Kisker, 2010). The president is the leader of the institution, who at first taught as faculty, but eventually left those duties to professors and tutors. At first, the president may take on many duties in the day-to-day operations of the college but as the college grows and more staff are hired, he will focus on "fundraising and community relations" (Cohen and Kisker, 2010) (Lucas,2006). At that time, college presidents were always White and male. In 1856, Martin Henry Freeman was named the first Black college president at Avery College. Francis Elizabeth Willard was named the first female college president at Evanston College for Ladies in Illinois in 1871.

In the American Colonial and Antebellum college era, faculty had the role of not only educating but also as disciplinarian. The faculty-student relationship was one of enemies (Lucas, 2006). According to Cohen and Kisker (2010), faculty were establishing themselves as respected professionals. Faculty were to develop curriculum and guide students. Today, faculty are professionals who teach and guide but are not responsible for discipline, there are other entities that handle disciplinary policies and action. Again, faculty were exclusively White and male until Charles L. Reason became the first Black person to teach at a mixed-race college in the US in 1849, and Patrick Francis Healy, while passing as a White man, became the first Black faculty member at the prestigious, predominantly white institution (PWI), Georgetown University in 1868. Harriet Cooke became the first female professor also in 1871 at Cornell College. She was appointed full professor and made equal pay to her male counterparts.

African Americans in U.S. Higher Education

Women and African Americans struggled to achieve educational opportunities at about the same time in American history. The Quakers and the Presbyterians supported African Americans in their educational attainment. In 1842, the Quakers created the Institute for Colored Youth which would later be named Cheyney State College. Lincoln University was founded by the Presbyterians in 1854 (Lucas, 2006). The support of education for African Americans started in the north. The notion of most whites in the south and many in the north was that blacks were inferior and should not be supported in their pursuit of education. "Southerners on the whole were willing to accede to the demands that educational opportunity be extended to Blacks, but only so long as it was not viewed as posing a frontal challenge to white supremacy or otherwise encouraging the Blacks to abandon his preordained 'place' in the social order" (Lucas, 2006).

Other supporters of this push for African Americans to have educational opportunities included "northern white benevolent societies, denominational missionary bodies, and private Black charitable organizations." The American Missionary Society financially supported a number of colleges for African Americans. The African American Methodist Episcopal Church also supported a number of colleges and universities for African Americans.

Particular institutions that were founded for African Americans include but are not limited to Howard University, Hampton Institute,

Clark University, and Morehouse College. "The original intent of most of the founders of Black colleges was to provide for their clientele an education indistinguishable from that commonly pursued by Whites.... liberal learning: Latin, Greek, and mathematics, supplemented by science, philosophy, history, astronomy, English composition and literature, and other curricular staples of New England liberal arts college." This was all happening despite some white supremacists believing Blacks were only good for sharecropping and other manual tasks (Lucas, 2006). Although some of the schools closed and some were reported as not adhering to the land-grant statutes, 101 Historically Black Colleges and Universities (HBCU) exist today (NCES, 2020). A great number of Black teachers, authors, celebrities, STEM professionals, and civil rights activists have graduated from HBCUs. While HBCUs have been consistently underfunded over the years, they continue to take the lead in addressing justice, equity, diversity, and inclusion work. This is not done in addition to providing educational experiences but the foundation. As reported by the Department of Education, 75% of Black doctoral graduates received their undergraduate degrees from HBCUs. While many colleges and universities are trying to figure out how to recruit and retain a diverse student body that includes those from different demographics and socio-economic status (SES), HBCUs have been doing this for well over 150 years. Not only that, the faculty also represent the student body with over half identifying as African American or Black. HBCUs were designed to be inclusive — to be a safe space. While there are some challenges, this still remains to be the case (Herr-Perin, 2021).

Higher education institutions are assessed by their accreditors on not only programs offered and cost but also on recruitment, retention, and graduation rates as well as the future success of their students' post-graduation. Institutions must demonstrate that they can not only recruit a good number of students but provide valuable experiences both inside and outside of the classroom. Not only that, but measuring learning outcomes, assessing activities that enhance learning, and making improvements in student learning and success based on those results (Kuh, 2009) are important. Three key concepts on student retention are integration, engagement, and resilience. The research on student success and retention is vast and reveals many ways in which institutions and students play a role in the higher education experience. Research on student success and retention models demonstrate how some effort is necessary on the part of the student and the institution in order to be successful. (Astin, 1984, 199, Banyard and Cantor, 2004; Kuh, 2009; Tinto, 2012). Student success encompasses both academic and social standing within the higher education experience; addressing both components in teaching, programming and policies positively impact student learning (Carini, Kuh, and Klein, 2006; Tinto, 2012).

The Faculty-Mentor

Faculty members play a significant role in the implementation of integration, engagement and resilience strategies. "Faculty interaction is central to student engagement" (Yearwood and Jones, 2012, p. 120). These interactions support the engagement process. The resilience concept also involves faculty, "Faculty mentors and other staff can help bolster protective factors" (Banyard and Cantor, 2004, p. 218). These concepts are not just about the individual student effort but include the influence and impact of faculty, staff, programs, and policies (Wolf- Wendel, Ward, and Kinzie, 2009).

The faculty-student mentoring relationship is valuable and unique, contributing to the education process; therefore, it is important to understand how students from diverse groups perceive the efficacy of the relationship. The literature on mentoring includes explorations into the faculty-student mentoring experiences of African American doctoral students (Barker, 2011; Felder & Barker, 2013; Gasman et al., 2008; Sethna, 2011).

Barker (2011), Felder and Barker (2013), and Gasman et al. (2008) specifically examined the experiences of African American doctoral students in predominantly White institutions (PWI). Facilitated by both qualitative and quantitative research methods, students and faculty shared their experiences and perspectives on the mentoring relationship. In each study, findings revealed that African American students who had positive experiences with their faculty-mentors believed those experiences contributed to their success in their doctoral program. Students who had negative mentoring experiences reported damage to their self-esteem (Barker, 2011; Felder & Barker, 2013; Gasman et al. 2008).

Students considered mentor and advisor relationships to be significant to their doctoral experiences. Both faculty and students considered race to be a significant aspect of the doctoral experience (Barker, 2011). Furthermore, the organizations that give oversight to public health programs also endorse the influence of diversity on faculty-student mentoring relationships.

Public Health

A degree in Public Health provides training in the following public health areas: epidemiology, biostatistics, research methods, health care management, environmental health, and social behavioral science. The bachelor's degree is more general with some concentration offerings. The master's degree is more specific to the different disciplines in public health. The doctoral degree options offer opportunities for research with a PhD or practice and leadership with a DrPH. With the focus on population as opposed to individuals, the public health workforce comprises various roles and positions and can work in government, nonprofit organizations, and healthcare organizations. The 10 Essential Services of Public Health outlines how public health professionals engage with the public. (See Chapter 4)

The Council on Education for Public Health (CEPH, 2011), the accrediting body for public health degree granting institutions, sets the standards and criteria for institutions that grant degrees in public health. Standard 1.8 Diversity, states, "The program shall demonstrate a commitment to diversity and shall evidence an ongoing practice of cultural competence in learning, research, and service practices" (CEPH, 2011, p. 11). According to the most recent school and program self-study reports submitted to CEPH, African American students are among those identified as an underrepresented minority (URM) in most of the accredited doctoral public health programs (CEPH, 2018). The Council for Education on Public Health requires concrete strategies for each accredited school or program to improve and maintain diversity at both the student and faculty level (CEPH, 2011). CEPH sets the standards for which all accredited graduate and undergraduate programs under its jurisdiction should meet. Standard 1.8 of the accreditation criteria for schools of public health delineates the importance of a commitment to diversity at both the student enrollment and faculty engagement level.

Standard 1.8 states, in part, 'Recognizing that graduates of public health programs may be employed anywhere in the world and work with many different populations, schools should provide a learning environment that prepares their students with broad skills regarding diversity and cultural competence, within the context of their own institution's mission statement. (CEPH, 2011, p. 11) It is in the best interest of public health programs to recruit, retain, and graduate a diverse group of students to meet accreditation criteria (CEPH, 2011). A diverse public health workforce helps to eliminate health disparities, thus advancing the public health field in the medical arena (Jackson, Homes, Golembiewski, Brown-Podgorski, & Menachemi, 2019). Not only that, representation at the faculty level is also needed.

Black Faculty at Predominantly White Institutions

Once they are faculty members, faculty of color face additional challenges. One of those challenges is that with the increase in students of color, there is an increase in mentoring, role modeling and advising as these students tend to seek out faculty of color to discuss their experiences with race and racism on campus. The other challenge is being seen and respected as a scholar by their non-white colleagues. They must put in more effort engaging with colleagues around research expectations. “Almost three-quarters of black, Asian and Latinx professors reported “feeling a need to work harder than their colleagues to be seen as legitimate scholars,” compared to less than half of white professors (Rucks-Ahidiana, 2019).

Faculty describe the work involved with the increase in student mentorship, advocating for themselves in the research space, and dealing with microaggressions is the invisible labor not considered during the tenure and promotion process (Masterson, 2021). Among Black academics, this invisible labor is called the "Black Tax.” This phrase originated from the experience of Black people who have advanced in socioeconomic status but had to often financially and emotionally support their family members. While the word "tax" is connected to finance, in this instance it measures psychological effort. It is the additional effort required to survive and advance in predominantly white institutions. For example, after the video aired of George Floyd's murder in May 2020, unbeknownst to many of our non-Black counterparts, many of us were emotionally spent. Many of us found ourselves trying to find ways to meet the emotional needs of our families, our students, and communities who were hurting while still teaching and attending meetings on Zoom, working with colleagues on research projects, and serving on committees. Not to mention we were still navigating through a global pandemic. Many of our White colleagues were oblivious to what we were experiencing, and we had neither the desire nor the bandwidth to educate them.

Shortly after, many institutions and businesses began releasing statements of solidarity. Many of them have policies and practices that are rooted in racism, but still continued to release statements, schedule open forums, town halls, and initiatives to create spaces where people can express themselves. There were new departments and divisions created focused on diversity, equity and inclusion (DEI). DEI consultants were brought in to educate their staff and engage in activities that would foster understanding and empathy around diversity. With these new initiatives, Black faculty, staff and students found themselves in the midst of doing more work. Now, many had to assist or even lead these efforts. "More than other faculty, they are called upon to be the race expert at their respective institutions" (Gray and Brooks, 2021, p. 3). There were two choices: 1) don't get involved, protect your time and sanity and risk the efforts being mismanaged and more harmful due to ignorance 2) get involved to ensure that the efforts were as helpful as possible while being emotionally exhausted. This is a constant choice that has to be made when it comes to racial justice efforts on college campuses.

There is a need for non-Black faculty to educate themselves on anti-racism. They need to gain understanding of institutional racism and how it impacts students and faculty of color. We must first acknowledge how many faculty are not trained in this manner. They get doctoral degrees in their content area; they are trained to conduct research. Some doctoral programs offer teaching and learning courses or certifications, but most faculty enter the academy having little to no teaching experience. Support for teaching is provided through the institutions teaching and learning centers and instructional design departments. Faculty receive o*n-the-job* training when it comes to teaching, advising and mentoring. It is usually for the faculty to pursue opportunities to learn about the cultural and racial experiences of their students.

It is beneficial for students to have faculty who are first generation students, who are immigrants, who are differently abled, or who are LGBTQ. It is also beneficial for students to have faculty of color. In fact, faculty of color are also first generation, differently abled, LGBTQ, and/or immigrants. Faculty who have had similar experiences can relate to students, understand their cultural differences or cultural perspectives. (Couture & Bang. 2022). But it is also important to have faculty who are non-people of color who make the effort to understand students' cultural perspectives, show empathy, and acceptance. If there are ideas and practices they do not understand, they should seek to understand. Being a mentor to students is not easy; it is not something that comes to most faculty naturally. It is something that has to be practiced and constantly assessed to make sure that students are receiving the support that is needed. Being a resource to students means that faculty have to take the time to be proactive about connecting students to services.

Faculty Saving Themselves and their Students

Black students and non-Black students benefit from having Black faculty in the classroom. They benefit from having access to faculty with varied experiences and backgrounds. Much of what faculty bring to the classroom is based on their own experiences. Students can benefit from engaging course material through different perspectives.

For non-white male students, representation matters. A student I am currently mentoring asked me, "why did I have to wait so long to finally have a professor who looks like me?" This question plays over and over in my head. As she and I work together on her career plan, I tell her about different opportunities and discuss the challenges and barriers she faces everyday as a Black student attending a predominantly white institution (PWI). I understand her because I've been where she is. I've experienced some of the same challenges. It's important for higher education institutions to put forth the effort in making sure that students have representation in the classroom and in administrative positions. These voices will make the institution better. There is a disparity in the presence of black faculty on college campuses; these disparities are even more so at the department level. For example, STEM departments have a dearth of Black faculty. Tenured and tenure track Black faculty are few and far between when we look at higher education institutions across the country. Many of the Black faculty are in adjunct or non-tenure track positions without a pathway to get into a tenure track position.

My primary research is on student perspectives and perceptions of their mentoring experiences, but I've included in this book some faculty perspectives sharing their own strategies and outlook on what mentoring black doctoral students should look. I've included some statements from faculty who have volunteered to share their strategies for effective mentorship. Hopefully this will be of help to those who are reading this text to understand some of the ways that faculty are doing this mentoring work on the ground. (See Chapter 6)

Conversely, the students who participated in this research expressed that they felt isolated, misunderstood, and that their ideas, vision, and goals were not valued by faculty. Some of the faculty relationships they described were lacking in support. While others expressed that they were supported and were mentored well. So, there are obviously some strategies that are working and some opportunities where faculty can improve as mentors. Much of what we do in higher education as faculty takes up quite a bit of our time. We have teaching, research, and service responsibilities. If there are no mechanisms in place to incentivize or support mentoring activities, faculty are adding mentoring to their workload. Faculty want to do an effective job but don't have the time to invest fully. Time was a common theme that emerged in the faculty and student research, respectively. The students shared about their challenges with scheduling time to meet with faculty and when meeting with them, there was only a short amount of time to focus on their work. Many times, faculty traveled to work on their own research.

Tenured and tenure-track faculty have three core responsibilities: teaching, research, and service to the institution and the discipline. In most higher education institutions, mentoring is considered a service activity. Mentoring can include teaching, research and/or career guidance. There is the burden of "invisible labor" for Black faculty who tend to make themselves available to Black students in need of guidance and support.

Making the time and exerting the extra effort on top of faculty responsibilities can lead to burnout. If we are working in institutions that are not inclusive, supportive spaces, it is very difficult for us to provide for those students while many of us are fighting our own battles with racism and discrimination. Many times, we manage to still support students in spite of the toll it takes on our health, physically and mentally. We have to acknowledge that this is happening. We have to address this challenge through systems change and that means changes to institutional policies, practices, and culture. Many institutions have the words on paper — supporting diversity, equity and inclusion — but the policies, practices and culture of the institution do not align with those written statements.

CHAPTER 3

The Value of Faculty Mentoring

Doctoral persistence and completion continue to be topics of interest in higher education.

Over half of all doctoral students do not persist and for those that do graduate, it can take anywhere from seven to ten years to complete the degree. For students of color, it is even more concerning. Higher education institutions continue to search for better ways to support doctoral students. Mentoring as well as having access to diverse faculty have shown to have an impact on the retention and completion of doctoral study for Black students. Therefore, it is important to apply this knowledge to the policies and practices in higher education, specifically in public health programs with the hope of improving their faculty-student interactions, which has an impact on doctoral persistence and diversity outcomes. For students moving through to the doctoral process, the goal is for them to be successful, to finish and move on to public health practice, research or teaching. This is the pipeline, and improving this pipeline is imperative to both higher education and the field of public health. There are still very low percentages of Black students and faculty in higher education.

There is extensive research that focuses on doctoral student success and it shows that faculty-student mentoring is one of the most significant factors. Black students who are successful in graduate programs are determined by their experiences. It can be very difficult for African American students to navigate predominantly White spaces where direct and indirect racism and discrimination may happen. Many persist despite their very racialized experiences. African American students may not receive the same enthusiasm and support for their research interests, which tend to focus on their own communities. In order for colleges and universities to do better with supporting Black doctoral students, it is important to understand their experiences and perspectives.

The Connection to Health

Eliminating health disparities is a priority for public health practitioners and researchers, which is parallel to the racial disparities that exist in doctoral programs in general and specifically in public health. Training a diverse group of public health practitioners, researchers, and educators is necessary in helping to meet this goal. When focusing on Public Health doctoral programs, Black students are in the minority in majority of the public health schools and programs - with the exception of Historically Black Colleges and Universities (HBCU), of which there are four accredited public health schools in the country. (Tennessee State, Jackson State, Tuskegee University, and Morehouse College) With mentoring being such a significant factor in Black students completing their doctoral programs, learning about these mentoring experiences will provide understanding to public health doctoral program administrators and faculty.

Institutional Support for Mentoring Activities

Frequently faculty go above and beyond to support students but do not have the support from the institution. Without there being systems in place to support faculty in developing effective mentoring relationships with their students, then it is possible to have some faculty invest in those relationships but others who choose not to do so. Faculty have their own challenges and barriers when it comes to mentoring students. (VanSchyndel et al., 2019). Faculty do not receive formal training in mentoring. Because of this many focus on tasks and roles instead of student learning. Students need assistance with transitioning from student to scholar to professional. This includes involving students in research, publishing in journals, presenting at conferences, and connecting students to financial support. Students look to mentors for guidance on the research process, careers, and other components of the "hidden curriculum" Faculty tend to have competing responsibilities including teaching, research, and students. Some faculty also hold administrative responsibilities. Faculty play different roles: advisor, supervisor, instructor— but that doesn't mean that they will be great mentors. This relationship can have a significant impact on the student experience and their progression.

Oftentimes, Black faculty have the additional burden to carry the load of diversity efforts on college campuses. The "minority tax" or "Black tax" is when Black faculty take on more service, teach more courses, and are always available — when their White colleagues do not share the same burden. Many choose to take on this work to ensure that students have access to them and to support their schools. Others may feel pressured to do so for the same reasons. Being the few on campus, Black students seek out Black faculty for mentoring and support. Some faculty shared their thoughts, perspectives and strategies they've used to support Black doctoral students. (See Chapter 6)

CHAPTER 4

The Public Health Field

According to the American Public Health Association (APHA), "Public health promotes and protects the health of people and the communities where they live, learn, work, and play. While a doctor treats people who are sick, those of us working in public health try to prevent people from getting sick or injured in the first place. We also promote wellness by encouraging healthy behaviors" (APHA, 2021). The work of promoting health and preventing disease is guided by the 10 essential services of public health that include:

1. Assess and monitor population health.
2. Investigate, diagnose, and address health hazards and root causes.
3. Communicate effectively to inform and educate.
4. Strengthen, support, and mobilize communities and partnerships.
5. Create, champion, and implement policies, plans and laws.
6. Utilize legal and regulatory actions.
7. Enable equitable access.
8. Build a diverse and skilled workforce.
9. Improve and innovate through evaluation, research, and quality improvement.

10. Build and maintain a strong organizational infrastructure for public health.

These 10 essential services fall within three core functions: assessment, policy development, and assurance. The three core functions and 10 essential services are the framework in which public health practitioners ensure that optimal health is accessible to the whole population.

Health equity is a major premise for public health practice. A common belief in the field of public health is that all members of the community are connected, therefore it is beneficial for all members of the community to have optimal health. We are a global society, so this is not only meant for US communities, but for communities throughout the world.

There are goals established for health in the United States. Every ten years since 1990, the Healthy People goals outline priorities and objectives based on the needs of the population.

Healthy People 2030 has just been released (Healthy People 2030 | health.gov). These are the goals we hope to accomplish by the year 2030. A team of public health and health professionals hold meetings to discuss the priorities for the next 10 years. They assess the previous 10 years and where we are as a nation. There were some goals set for 2020, some we have made great strides in, while others we need to vastly improve. Over the years our focus has been mainly chronic diseases like obesity, diabetes, and asthma, which require daily management and connection to health services.

Social Determinants of Health (SDOH) is a significant factor in all health outcomes. SDOH is defined as the conditions in which we live, work, learn, and play and includes demographic information like race, gender, zip code, and other non-medical factors that influence health and health outcomes (WHO, 2021).

Health Disparities are "preventable differences in the burden of disease, injury, violence, or opportunities to achieve optimal health that are experienced by socially disadvantaged populations" (CDC, 2021). For Black people in the U.S., there are disparities in chronic health conditions, such as cancer, mental health, infant mortality, healthcare access, and now COVID-19 —which Black people are at increased risk for contracting the virus —and dying from complications of the virus.

Many of these disparities have to do with social determinants of health, which has to do with systemic racism. The phrase "zip code determines your health" touches on this very issue. Where we live has a significant impact on our health-whether or not we live in areas of increased violence, a food desert with a fast-food establishment on every corner, near power plants, and no safe place to walk or bike. Living in areas with green space, access to affordable fresh fruits and vegetables, safe biking and walking paths has been linked to more positive health outcomes. Students grow up in these diverse types of environments and many times this is the reason they pursue degrees in public health. They want to help people; they want to help communities.

Public Health in Higher Education

Public health is unique in that it is interdisciplinary by nature and functions collaboratively with other fields. There are multiple disciplines within the field of public health: epidemiology, biostatistics, environmental health, social behavioral science, and health policy and management. There are opportunities for graduate students to pursue dual degrees in business, public policy, law, dentistry, medicine, nursing, and more. A student who graduates with a public health degree (undergraduate or graduate) can find themselves in various industries and sectors. For this reason, many students are overwhelmed by the options and opportunities and have a challenging time explaining to their parents what they can do with the degree once they graduate. Having mentors and access to faculty and professionals in the field helps students in receiving the guidance they need to make decisions about their future.

During this COVID-19 global pandemic, the field of public health is on center stage. Even more than it was for the Zika and Ebola outbreaks. The attention may be on par with the HIV/AIDS outbreak in the 1980s. The field of public health has grown and as a result there is a demand for training and the number of schools and programs of public health in the United States has also increased. There are certificate programs and courses as well. Public health is a rapidly growing field because of the increased interest in disease prevention, health promotion, and healthcare in general (Koblinsky et al., 2015). Current faculty members in public health programs are approaching retirement (Jackson et al., 2019). There is a shortage of doctoral graduates to fill the gap left by long time faculty members who have been a part of the public health infrastructure (Jackson et al., 2019). Furthermore, doctoral graduates do not feel adequately prepared for academia (Koblinsky et al., 2015).

It is important for health professionals to stay in tandem with the national demographic, but at this time that is not the case. "Little progress has been made in achieving a critical mass of underrepresented minority (URM) academicians in the public health workforce" (Annang et al., 2010, p. 39). Much of the research on URM in the healthcare professions focuses on the need for recruitment and retention in clinical professions (Baldwin et al., 2006). However, the problem also exists in the public health academy responsible for training the future public health workforce. One of the objectives set forth by Healthy People 2020 (Office of Disease Prevention and Health Promotion, 2019) is to decrease racial health disparities throughout the United States and do this by increasing efforts to recruit those who have been systemically excluded from the public health workforce.

In order to gain insight into the experiences of URM faculty members and discuss best practices and challenges, the Association of Schools of Public Health (ASPH) convened a retreat with 70 faculty members from 36 accredited schools and eight programs of public health across the nation in 2006 (Annang et al., 2010). Thirty-four of the faculty members were randomly selected to complete a survey. The themes that emerged as a result included: (1) conveying the significance of discussing limited diversity in the public health academy; (2) offering a safe environment to openly dialogue; (3) offering forums for discussion periodically; (4) presenting an opportunity for URM faculty to network and connect with one another; and (5) prioritizing recruitment and retention of URM faculty in public health (Annang et al., 2010, p. 40).

This type of forum was described as empowering for African American faculty. African American faculty members shared insights on how institution leaders can recruit and retain URM faculty and suggested that institutions not only express the importance of doing so but make recruitment of URM a priority (Annang et al., 2010).

Haizlip (2012) presented a problem within the counseling and psychology doctoral degree programs that is linked to the African American students who graduate with doctoral degrees in counseling or psychology. Haizlip presented data that demonstrated that African American students are seeking doctoral degrees but are not pursuing professorships.

Recommendations for addressing this problem are to provide mentoring for African American doctoral students that would provide socialization into the professorate; take specific steps to retain current African American faculty; and have students more involved in their learning, providing opportunities for faculty to give feedback. This can serve as an example for public health doctoral degree programs.

A primary public health goal outlined by Healthy People 2020 is to "achieve health equity, eliminate disparities, and improve the health of all groups" (Office of Disease Prevention and Health Promotion, 2019, p. 1). The preparation and training of a diverse public health workforce is a means to achieve this goal (ASPH, 2011; Cohen & Steinecke, 2006). In many colleges and universities, there is a lack of diversity when it comes to certain races and ethnicities (Cargill, 2009; Felder & Barker, 2013; Scharff & Kreuter, 2000).

There is an even greater disparity within schools and programs of public health. African Americans are underrepresented among graduates of public health doctoral programs (ASPH, 2011). A study was conducted on ASPPH members - schools and programs of public health. Over the course of 20 years, from 1996 to 2006, the number of members increased from 27 to 105. When polling the 27 members in 1996, of the students enrolled in their public health programs, 8.3% were Black. This includes both undergraduate and graduate programs. For doctoral degrees conferred that year, 2.5% were Black students. According to the census in 1996 Blacks made up 12.8% of the US population or 38 million people. In 2016, the doctoral degrees conferred for Black students went up 3.9 percentage points. According to the census in 2016, Blacks made up 13% of the US population or more than 40 million people.

After reviewing the low percentage growth of Black doctoral student graduation rates, it will not be surprising to notice how low Black faculty rates are in public health. Based on the ASPPH membership, 3.6% of public health faculty were Black and 2.2% were tenured in 1997 and that percentage decreased as they increased in rank from Assistant Professor to Associate Professor to Full Professor. In 2016 there was an increase of 1.5 percentage points. Dr. Jose' Ramon Hernandez-Pena, president of the American Public Health Association (APHA), considers the lack of diversity in the public health workforce, a public health problem within itself considering the challenges with health disparities in the US (Fernandez-Pena, 2021). With the increase in undergraduate students in public health including an increase in Black students, there is the potential to have that increase continue to the graduate level and eventually to the professoriate and leadership positions. Exposure can be one way to increase students who seek out public health as a major (Smith & Young, 2020). Public health has always suffered from an "identity crisis" in that many people do not know what public health is, what it entails, and what public health professionals do. Even with the pandemic, the general population still has very little understanding of public health, population health, and prevention. So, exposure at young ages to public health topics and public health professionals would address that knowledge gap.

However, the glaring issue with low percentages of Black students in health professions' graduate programs has much to do with systemic racism (Johnson, Spivey, & Chisholm-Burns.2021). There are policies and procedures in place that create challenges and barriers for Black students. The same is for Black faculty in general and specifically for those in public health.

As a former director of a public health graduate program, I witnessed first-hand the challenges that Black students faced in the admissions process. I also noticed the recruitment process was lacking in purposeful recruitment of students from minoritized backgrounds in general. In contrast, there was purposeful recruitment of international students that included research and financial incentives to ensure that our school was their first choice. For Black students, I did not see the same effort. As the director, I used my network in my recruiting efforts. I had very little in my recruiting budget at the time, so I had to be creative. I noticed that we had many Black students who were in the undergraduate program, and I was the only one having conversations with them about graduate school. Many of these students were considered "nontraditional," in that they had jobs, sometimes more than one, and they had familial responsibilities. This did not stop me from encouraging them, as I also had a full-time job in graduate school in addition to a child. My students knew this about me, and this was an example to them that it could be done. However, I noticed that the research and financial opportunities were not going to them. A robust undergraduate program is a perfect funnel for a graduate program, but it seemed that only certain students were encouraged to pursue graduate education.

The other issue with recruitment was how graduate school fairs and open houses were used. For both, there was no purposeful strategy for inviting and welcoming students from minoritized backgrounds. It was not until I made relationships with Historically Black Colleges and Universities (HSBC) that we increased the diversity in the program. One year, I traveled from Philadelphia to Atlanta, GA to Clark Atlanta University, Morehouse College, and Spellman College, otherwise known as The Triangle, for a graduate school fair. I was able to speak with students, faculty, and advisors about our program. These were strong students doing great work in their programs and in the field. I did not go to a HBCU, but I understand the value of HBCUs and the excellence of the students they produce. Each year, I also went to Cheyney University and Lincoln University to recruit. I built relationships with their staff and was invited to many events, and the students began to know me and could call me if they had any questions about their graduate application.

The next challenge was the graduate application process, specifically the use of the GRE as an assessment tool. Our admissions motto was that "we take a portfolio approach to reviewing applications," meaning we consider all aspects including transcripts, test scores and experience. However, I noticed two things with the GRE, 1) how heavily the admission committee weighed it and 2) how low the scores were for students coming from HBCUs. I had already conducted research on GRE scores in general and knew how they are not always an accurate depiction of the students' ability to do graduate work. Some faculty believe that the math scores are telling of the students' ability to do well in Biostatistics, a core public health course. In addition to my general research on GRE scores, I found that students who attend HBCUs have lower scores based on inadequate preparation for the exam. So, I started doing GRE info sessions for students. For students in the application pipeline, as the director of the program, I had the authority and discretion to write exemption letters for those students who had high GPAs with high grades in stats and writing classes, and strong recommendation letters. I truly took a portfolio approach to reviewing the applications for all of them. The students did not know about the exemption letters. However, one student found out years later and wrote me a letter:

Hi, Natasha: I hope this message finds you well. I've been meaning to contact you for a while. It's been four years since I came up to your office in XXX Hall and we spoke about being enrolled in the MPH program. I wasn't aware of it until recently, but XXXX told me what you did for me so that I could get into the program. I wanted to thank you for vouching for me. I just wanted you to know that I graduated this past December with a 3.61 GPA, and I became a research assistant for XXX during my final year and a half (and I am still working with her now).

Perhaps XXXX didn't see my potential, but you did. I hope I made you proud! All the best, XXX

When making strides towards diversity, inclusion, and belonging, we cannot just say we value it, we must match it with actions. Purposeful recruitment and retainment are key to attracting and educating Black students. When you make the decision to meet the needs of your most marginalized students, you meet the needs of all your students. Everyone benefits. The same goes for faculty. Examine the policies and procedures and the culture of your departments, schools, and institutions. Are they not only inclusive, but do they support this idea of belonging? Are people able to show up as themselves or do they need to change some aspects of their appearance, personality, and presence in order to "fit in?" For me, I knew to go to HBCUs to recruit students into our graduate program. However, after I was no longer in that position, that recruitment ceased. Diversity decreased in the graduate program. Had this been a part of the strategic plan, it would not matter if I was in the position or not. Programs need sustainable recruitment and retention plans. If faculty and staff are involved in the development of the strategic plan, they can be a part of the work being done to ensure that maintaining diversity at both the student and the faculty level is a priority.

As a leader, you may have to make decisions and step outside of the box to meet the needs of students. What would it take for you as a leader to be proactive in how you help students who have been traditionally marginalized? What does it take to make you do that? Is it on the faculty or staff or is there something the institution can do to ensure or enable faculty and staff to support students?

CHAPTER 5

Student Mentoring Experiences

Doctoral Student Experiences

Racially minoritized doctoral students have unique experiences throughout their academic experiences. These experiences include recruitment and admissions, academic advising, residential life, classroom instruction, financial experiences, and dissertation research. All these experiences can have an impact on the success and completion of the doctoral program as well as future career opportunities. The field of study also plays a significant role in how these experiences play out.

The following section of this chapter describes a qualitative research project that was conducted to explore the experiences of African American doctoral students in public health and their perceptions of the faculty mentoring they received while conducting their dissertation research (Patterson, 2020). This basic qualitative research study used semi structured interviews that allowed for broad descriptions of the participants' experiences to gain understanding about the faculty mentoring relationship in doctoral public health programs. Qualitative research methods are utilized to provide a platform for sharing stories of marginalized groups. Qualitative methods allow participants to share their stories in their own voice (Woodley & Lockard, 2016).

Qualitative methods are holistic in approach and the researcher, a human being, is the instrument (Woodley & Lockard, 2016). Participants completed a semi structured interview with standard open-ended questions so that all participants were asked the same questions but allowed to freely share their thoughts and elaborate with examples. The qualitative methodology was a good fit for the questions under consideration because it allowed participants to provide a more comprehensive response, giving detail to the already existing quantitative research on mentoring and doctoral students (Davis, 2007; Dixon-Reeves, 2003; Gasman et al., 2008).

Basic qualitative designs answer the question why and focus on providing a space for participants who are usually marginalized to share their perspectives. The semi structured interviews included a protocol, instructions, interview questions, and probing phrases like "Tell me more," "Please explain," and "How so?" Merriam (2009) explained this type of research as a means to learn about the experiences of participants and the meanings participants attach to those experiences. With this design, it was easier to spend more time investigating the thoughts and feelings of African American doctoral students. The results provide an in depth look at the experiences of African American doctoral students currently enrolled in public health doctoral programs.

The participants in this study were nine African American students currently enrolled in public health doctoral programs in the United States. Each participant was in the dissertation phase of the program at the time of the study and was currently working one-on-one with a faculty-mentor or advisor. Some doctoral programs use the words advisor, chair, or mentor to describe the faculty member who takes the lead role in providing guidance during the student's research experience (Lechuga, 2011). For the purposes of this book, mentor and advisor were interchangeable terms. Stage 3 of the doctoral experience focuses not only on the transition to becoming an independent researcher, but also the shift in identity as students transition in preparation for academic professions upon completion of their degree (Baker & Pifer, 2011). The support provided by faculty-mentors during this process has an impact on students' overall success.

While participants were allowed to elaborate and provide details and examples, each participant was asked the same questions using the same wording. Asking each participant, the same questions brought validity and authenticity to the data collection process (Merriam, 2009).

The questions focused on the mentor-mentee relationship, expectations for the mentoring relationship, and persistence to graduation for students pursuing a doctoral degree in public health. Creswell (2007) suggested five to seven open ended questions to give participants options in how they respond and how much they choose to share about their perspectives and experiences.

The first interview question was not a question but a request for participants to "share some thoughts on your experience with the faculty member who has been assigned as your mentor." According to Qu and Dumay (2011), starting the interview with a request for this information is meant to start the interview quickly and follow up with the main questions. The opening question allowed participants to begin by giving a summary of their overall experience with their faculty-mentor, chair, or advisor. Participants shared their experience on how or why the faculty member was assigned by the program or selected by the student. Participants shared about their interactions with the faculty member and their experiences with communication and feedback received from the faculty member.

The second question, considered to be a specifying question (Qu & Dumay, 2011), was meant to explore the participants' initial expectations for their faculty-mentor: "What did you expect from the mentoring relationship at the onset?" Participants shared their thoughts and perceptions about the faculty member in question and their relationship with that faculty member. The expectations for the mentor relationship set the tone for the interaction between the participant and their faculty-mentor. The participants also discussed whether they knew what to expect from the relationship. The second question spoke to the research that found that doctoral students have little information about the process, faculty, and the mentoring relationship's impact on their dissertation progress, especially for African American students (Felder, 2010).

Student Mentoring Experiences

The third question allowed the participant to reflect on their experience and the dissertation process and the role of the faculty-mentor in that process: "How have your experiences with your faculty-mentor influenced your persistence through your doctoral program?" Participants reflected on their doctoral student experience and their relationship with their faculty-mentor. Participants were free to share their perceptions about how and if their faculty-mentor impacted their ability to persist through the doctoral process. In response to the third question, participants described the challenges or barriers, strategies, and positive ways their faculty members supported them or the ways in which they did not feel supported.

The fourth question asked, "How does mentoring relate to your positive or negative experiences as a doctoral student in this program?" As reported by Barker (2011), "the racial climate for Black graduate or doctoral students may be a reaction of the student's interaction with the institution, department, and individuals (i.e., faculty and other students)" (p. 389). Dixon-Reeves (2003) highlighted the significance of faculty mentorship to African American graduate students' academic and professional development. The fourth interview question was used to gain insight into the mentoring experiences of African American doctoral students in public health.

The fifth question asked participants to "explain any challenges or barriers, if any, that you have experienced that interfered with your doctoral progress." The fifth question was designed to capture a glimpse into the lived experiences of the African American doctoral student participants to glean what may slow their process or make it difficult for them to complete the doctoral program. Participants had the option of not answering the question or stating that they did not perceive any challenges or barriers. The researcher provided examples to participants to prompt their memory of any such challenges or barriers. The examples included mentioning advisors, mentors, courses, the dissertation process, research, administrative issues, and personal life issues. Participants also shared their experiences based on what they identified as a barrier or challenge to their completion that did not have anything to do with their mentor.

The sixth question asked participants to "explain whether or not you feel that your race has positively or negatively influenced your mentoring experiences in your doctoral program." The student experience can be impacted by whether students feel welcomed and valued in the academic community. If a student perceives their value to be impacted by racial perception or bias, they may start to question their abilities (Felder et al., 2014). Within this question, students were also asked about their dissertation research topics and if their topics were about race or ethnicity in some way. Participants were also asked if their mentor supported and understood their research topic if it was race or ethnicity related. Felder et al. (2014) discussed how African American students tend to conduct research on their own communities with the hope of advancing and strengthening the communities they represent. Felder et al. stated that "African American students carry the weight of wanting to improve education for their communities and this obligation is deeply intertwined with their research agendas" (p. 25).

The sample included nine public health doctoral students from multiple institutions who self-identified as African American. The participants' ages ranged from 24 to 40 years old. Each participant had completed doctoral coursework, passed their comprehensive exams, and was currently in the dissertation phase, or Stage 3, of their program. Of the nine participants, two were enrolled in online PhD programs. The other seven participants were enrolled in traditional, brick and mortar PhD programs. Four participants were able to seek out their dissertation chair or mentor and select that faculty member to guide their dissertation process. Five of the participants were assigned to specific faculty members by their programs. Two of the participants who had faculty members assigned to them received a change in chair assignment during the course of their research or dissertation writing process. One participant was pursuing a DrPH while the other participants were pursuing a PhD. The student who was pursuing a DrPH still had a final written document that required her to work closely with a faculty member for guidance, feedback, and approval. One participant's faculty-mentor was also African American, while the other eight faculty-mentors were White.

Figure 4. Codes and thematic categories.

In Figure 4, the codes are connected to the themes that are highlighted in various colors. The mapping demonstrates the connections between codes and themes. The codes are based on the participant responses and consist of the statements and phrases that were similar in nature. Some of the codes were connected to different themes. For example, the theme, Cultural Capital encompassed the codes, Support and Guidance, which is also connected to the theme, Faculty Mentor Expectations. Seeking out other faculty and faculty from minoritized backgrounds is linked to both Cultural Capital and Race.

With the list of both starter codes and emergent codes, the researcher began to connect the codes that were similar, using thematic categories. There are 12 codes: Time, Guidance, Faculty Assignment, Encouragement, Spoken and Unspoken Norms,

Seeking out other faculty, Faculty from minoritized backgrounds, Research Topic, Anxiety, Self-Doubt, Diversity in the Classroom, and Loneliness. Each code was based on phrases used by the participants. The phrases that were similar in nature, focusing on the same topic or issue, were coded with a term or phrase that best described each. The codes were collapsed into overarching themes. Six major themes, color highlighted in Figure 4, are discussed in the following sections: Cultural Capital, Faculty Mentor Expectations, Knowledge and Information, Race, Diversity, and Mental Health. Based on the findings from the six questions, probing questions were asked to delve deeper into the responses; the probing questions revealed several codes. The codes and themes are presented below.

Thematic Categories

Cultural Capital

Cultural capital includes the codes: support, guidance, encouragement, and seeking out other faculty members. Cultural capital is a theme that emerged based on codes that focused on the skills and knowledge the students possessed and used to their advantage to meet their needs and persist through their program. Cultural capital, developed by sociologist Pierre Bourdieu (1984) in the study of social inequality, is "having tangible and intangible assets that give us social mobility, not related to income, net worth or financial measure" (Yosso, 2005, p. 70). There are three types or states of cultural capital: institutionalized, embodied, and objectified. The institutionalized state is about educational qualifications, certifications, rankings, and job titles. The embodied state encompasses attitudes, beliefs, language, and intentions. The objectified state is "cultural goods, such as books, paintings, or musical instruments" (Cincinnato et al., 2016, p. 145).

Cultural wealth, differentiated from financial wealth that is focused on financial capital, is measured by what was described by Yosso (2005) as aspirational, navigational, social, linguistic, familial, and resistant capital. Cultural capital supports the idea that marginalized groups, especially people of color, bring with them tools and strategies that stem from consistently having to make do with fewer resources. Theme 1 emerged from the participants' descriptions of their experiences and how some were able to navigate around the challenges and barriers they faced. The codes that led to this theme include seeking out other faculty members for guidance, support, and encouragement, in addition to identifying strategies that enabled students to demand time and attention from their faculty mentor. Two participants had challenges with their faculty mentor but did not discuss the ways they were able to navigate around those challenges; they did not seek out other faculty or peers for assistance.

Some of the participants used their abilities to network and engage with other faculty members and build relationships with them. Participants stated how they needed to learn or identify strategies for getting their needs met when they were not receiving support from their faculty mentor.

P1 stated that, “I had to just learn to bother the heck out him to get what I needed because waiting for him to respond or trying to be polite just didn’t work.” P1 also stated that, “I learned to just bother him or just go to his assistant and put a meeting on his calendar and show up at his office.”

P2 looked to other faculty members for support, “I find myself turning to other faculty members for content related or technical support.” P2 was unsure if this is an acceptable practice,

“If I’m consulting with somebody else more than my advisors, sometimes I worry about, “well she’s my advisor; she should be the main person I should be communicating with, "but sometimes I don’t communicate with her as much as I do with other people.”

P3 also looked to other faculty members for assistance: “So, it is more on an individual level basis that you find a Black informal mentor or person that you can lean on or talk to. And thankfully, I have found that the people who are there are amazing and have been willing to let a student that is not their academic advisee, or their student come in and sit in their office to talk about what challenges they are facing.”

Similarly, P6 had to make inroads with her faculty mentor. “I had to really work at trying to email and talk with her as far as trying to get her over the phone.” However, “after the initial part of expressing that and making it known, it has over time gotten better.”

For P5, the embodied state of cultural capital emerged through his attitude and intentions: "I have good relationships with pretty much anyone in my department. I made it abundantly clear when I [came] to (School) that I wasn't going to change for anyone."

P5 shared what gives him pride: "That is one of the things I am proudest of being here is that they embrace my purpose, which is about improving equity; it's about making sure there's more people of color in this space."

P5 acknowledged that his experience may not be typical: "I recognize that it's not the typical case for students of color in this school; I get that, so I make no bones about it. My experience has been unusual, relative to even my contemporaries who had to leave because they didn't have the support that they needed."

P5 explained his desire to influence those around him: "It's actually just deepened and strengthened since I've been here. Not because of any adversity; I think it's because I've had the opportunity to introduce this perspective of being Black in America, being Black in academia not just in this space, but outside this door.'

P5's attitude and beliefs shape his ability to persist, "I made them acknowledge my thought and my perspectives, which goes beyond diversity; that's now inclusion, then there's equity."

Faculty mentor expectations

At the start of each interview two items were acknowledged. There was a discussion about whether the participants were able to select their faculty mentor or if their faculty mentor was assigned to them. Five of the participants selected and sometimes applied to a specific institution because of a certain faculty member with whom they wanted to work. The other four had their faculty mentor assigned to them when they enrolled in the doctoral program. The researcher also engaged in a discussion with some of the participants who had to change faculty mentors because their original faculty mentor left the institution. Two of the participants had a change in faculty mentors while working on their dissertation.

The participants shared their expectations for their faculty mentors throughout the interview discussions. When asked to identify their expectations for their faculty mentor, some participants shared that they did not know what to expect at the start of the doctoral program or dissertation process. Each of the participants in the study were the first in their families to pursue higher education at the doctoral level; some were the first to pursue higher education in general. When asked the question about what they expected coming into the process, the first-generation participants did not know anything outside of what they might have been told in a student orientation. Participants indicated a lack of guidance from family related to their doctoral process.

Participants used the word "support" and phrases that included the word "support." Some participants described their faculty mentor as supportive while some participants expressed a desire for more support. Participants provided examples of support like assisting students with decision-making related to their research, which methods to use, or narrowing down their research topic. One participant made sure to stress that her idea of support was "not handholding" but help with the different parts of the dissertation and writing. P8 mentioned having support from the first mentor, but not the second mentor, whom she received when her first mentor left the institution.

For the code "time," some participants mentioned how their faculty mentors had very little time. Faculty mentors may have been working on other projects, teaching, or traveling. However, time was not mentioned as an expectation; rather, time was mentioned in the context of understanding that faculty members were busy. The participants perceived time constraints as a norm in higher education. Participants discussed the ways in which they worked around their faculty mentor's schedule in order to achieve their goals, making statements like, "I had to just learn to bother the heck out of him to get what I needed because waiting for him to respond or trying to be polite didn't work." Of the nine participants, four participants specifically mentioned that their faculty mentors were very busy. Participants would preface their statements with, "I know faculty are busy." P2 shared her thoughts on mentoring, stating that it is the "most important relationship."

Since students are working independently on their research and no longer attending classes, "that person really drives how you feel about the program itself." P2 stated again how "faculty are busy" and that fact posed one of her biggest challenges. P2 shared her frustration with her mentor being unresponsive to emails, unavailable for meetings, "flying around the world," and how she had to learn to be persistent with communication and when making appointments for meetings.

Participants expressed that it was their responsibility, as the student, to navigate around the faculty mentor's time constraints. None of the participants demanded additional time or access. Participants all described the ways they successfully or unsuccessfully attempted to fit into the faculty mentor's schedule or persisted without the help of the mentor.

P6 shared, "I know for me, I am the type of person that when it comes to when I have certain questions that need more explanations, doing it through email doesn't always work for me because I have to talk it through or communicate verbally.

Two participants did not specifically mention time, but three mentioned how their faculty mentor is available to them.

P1 made a differentiation between the faculty member who advised students on their class schedule and other academic issues and the faculty member who became the lead advisor for her dissertation research. In Participant 1's case, the faculty member who provided academic advisement was also her dissertation advisor and chair of her dissertation committee. P1's expectations for this faculty member included providing career advice, space to share ideas, guidance on her academic plan, "guide me through my course selections, make sure that I stay on track, make sure that I am going to graduate on time. Guidance on my dissertation…just make sure I got through the process and didn't lag." P1 expressed how she needed clear instructions on what was required for the dissertation and advice about her career, "Let me know what they were looking for and what they weren't looking for. Then, just career advice when I was trying to figure out what I was going to do with this degree."

When asked how the relationship with the faculty mentor influenced persistence, P1 mentioned that she appreciated the faculty mentor providing support and encouragement, especially when she felt like she could not get through the program. The faculty mentor would respond with statements like, "you'll be fine," and showed empathy and understanding with, "we all go through this, it's a part of it (the process)." P1 saw her faculty mentor as a part of her support system. P1 saw this kind of support as something necessary for her to successfully persist through the program.

P1 shared how a previous academic advisor did not seem to care at about her progress and was grateful for her current advisor. P1 considered the faculty advisor or mentor her only connection to the university. "You aren't really interacting with other students, so I think that the person really drives how you feel about the program itself." Faculty time was an issue, "faculty are busy, and I think that could be the biggest challenge," but P1 identified the strategies for overcoming this challenge, although it was very frustrating. "I just had to learn to bother the heck out of him." She also contacted his assistant to scheduled meetings. P1 first questioned whether this method would be appropriate but after seeing results, she considered it a successful way to get her needs met.

With a dissertation topic focused on cultural competency, P1 received support from her dissertation committee and advisor, but she felt it was because she was able to select faculty who would be interested in that topic. She purposefully identified faculty whose work was focused on the area of cultural competency and is the primary reason why P1 selected her institution and doctoral program. She shared concerns for her classmates who were not having positive experiences with their faculty mentors. P1 believed that her situation, having a faculty mentor

who is supportive, accessible, and understanding, is not an usual experience for students in the program.

P1 shared additional comments after all formalized questions were asked. P1 reiterated how the mentor plays a key role since at this stage of the dissertation process, there is no other connection to the program and school. "And particularly if you are trying to keep students of color, having more Black faculty helps, because that's where people go; if you're interested in doing things around race, there are typically minority faculty that are doing this type of research."

When asked about the diversity at the institution where she attended, P1 stated, "there is a lack of diversity and if you look at percentages, but there was enough for me to get the experience that

I wanted…He (her advisor) had so many people who wanted to work with him because he was a minority. He would try to say yes to everyone, but then he was stretched too thin and sometimes he just did students a disservice because he didn't have time."

When asked about expectations, P2 expressed her appreciation for her current faculty mentor saying, "she believes in me and thinks that I'm a capable individual…she is someone who I could see being able to vouch for me like when it comes to interactions with other people, like other faculty…she would be the one to stand up for me."

P2 mentioned that she and her mentor do not have time to meet. The mentor travels frequently. "We do meet from time to time, but we don't have a regular standing meeting. We are trying to establish every two weeks but her schedule [does not always allow for it]." Despite the schedule conflicts, P2 felt that she and her mentor had good communication "for the most part."

P2's expectations for the mentoring relationship included having "matching" research interests so they could work together on research projects. Unfortunately, P2 had never worked with her faculty mentor on any projects because they do not share similar research interests. "She's interested in social determinants of health, which is what I'm interested in, but most of her interests are with gender, HIV/AIDS, which is not anything remotely what I'm interested in." P2 stated that she wanted a mentor who would have a similar research interest. P2 was unable to work with her faculty mentor on other research projects, only her dissertation research. P2 developed her dissertation research topic based on her own interests. She reported feeling disconnected from her faculty mentor and her classmates who did share interests with her faculty mentor and were able to work on research projects with her faculty mentor.

P2 did not think that her mentoring experiences influenced her persistence even though at times she felt that she "didn't really have the guidance" she needed. Again, P2 mentioned how she looked to other faculty members to assist her with decision making about her research. Since her research was something she developed based on her interest, she thought that her faculty mentor was "not as invested" as she would be had it been the mentor's own research or on a topic of interest to the mentor. "It's been a little bit of a challenge getting them (chair and committee) to be engaged enough to know what's going on and then be able to give good input…sometimes I ask questions, but I don't get answers" P2 noted. The issue of faculty time came up when discussing P2's need for more guidance. When speaking about faculty, P2 stated, "they are very busy people." She reiterated her practice of going to other faculty members to get her questions answered.

P2 shared some thoughts about expectations for her faculty mentor. P2 hoped to be "matched with someone, our research overlaps, and we would work on similar things." With respect to having time to meet, P2 shared, "she travels; most of her research is international. That makes it a little difficult to kind of have a standing meeting in place." More specifically, the expectation of time and accessibility seemed to be a challenge: "One expectation [was] that I would be able to work on her projects or maybe in terms of being able…more of the technical expertise of mentorship…Sometimes I ask questions, but I don't get answers…umm yeah, faculty are busy, and I think that could be the biggest challenge."

P3 had a previous relationship with her faculty mentor; they worked together on her master's thesis. "We had already grown familiar with each other; he seemed like the right fit, so it's been a great working experience." P3's dissertation topic involved race and her mentor provided support "in hearing me and supporting me and engaging in conversations with me that could be perceived as really challenging given the dynamics of gender and race, and the topic area."

P3 had an expectation of receiving critical feedback, "I want to know if I'm doing something wrong, if there's room for improvement, and when you don't ever get that you don't know the truth. I am not perfect but there's more feedback I could be getting that I'm missing out on."

P4's expectations focused on time and communication with her faculty mentor. P4 stated that she "wanted her faculty mentor to be responsive to me. And I guess as you go through the dissertation phase, you know people who've had mentors; you've heard of sometimes, experiences where they haven't been as good. They kind of felt a disconnect between the mentor and the student. So, in that regard I was hoping that the person would be totally opposite."

P4 was able to have regular communication with her mentor. "After our conference calls I felt reenergized to continue the work." However, she still felt alone in the experience, "It's good, it's been good, but it's still…, she doesn't handhold, so it's still kind of like, on the one hand it's a good experience but I still feel like I'm out here by myself."

P5 had a change in faculty mentors. The first one he perceived to be not as supportive. "She has outright stated that she isn't able to read me. She doesn't know whether I'm upset, whether I'm cool. P5 perceived the new faculty mentor to be more supportive, helpful, and understanding. "She's very meticulous which is very different from my old advisor. I need meticulous at this point in the game. I actually appreciate that about her, although it gets very annoying when you get feedback, but I appreciate it in the long run…I certainly wanted their guidance through this process."

Since his current faculty mentor is also African American, P5 had an expectation that the faculty mentor would be able to guide him in the academic space being a person of color. He had questions like: "What is like being a person of color in the academy, things like that. What should I look out for? What are the things that I can do to make sure that my color isn't a barrier to any of the opportunities I am able to explore?"

P5 already had research experience and a published paper, so he was familiar with that aspect of the research process. He looked to his faculty mentor for help navigating the doctoral process since this was a new space for him. P5 was the first in his family to get to this level of education. He stated how everything was new and he had no foundation for how to be a successful doctoral student.

When P6 was asked about her expectations for her faculty mentor, she responded, "I honestly was expecting what the handbook said that that mentor would do, like you are supposed to communicate with your mentor on a regular basis, whether that be weekly or every other week, whatever you find that is suitable for you both."

P6's focus was on effort and communication and she spoke about not wanting to have to pressure her faculty mentor into doing what is expected.: "And it is really like both people have to be willing to put into it. So, you don't want to make anybody do anything that they don't want to do, but at the same time, hopefully the mentor will be able to guide you."

P6 also shared her thoughts about internal motivation: "That's the level of importance, communication being at 100% with the doctoral program. Most of the students are driven within themselves; at that level you don't need someone to hold their hand but be willing to be of assistance."

P7 expressed frustration with not having the support and wanting to quit the program.

"I think I would have stayed in it, I would have stuck with it, had we had the right supports internally, but we didn't. It was such a fight. There was fighting on all sides and I just didn't have the energy for it."

P7 explained how much effort she put into searching for a faculty mentor, hoping to work with someone who would be supportive, "We jumped mountains just to get a credible, knowledgeable chair and the supporting committee members that we needed for my direct dissertation."

It was important for P7 to know what is expected and having this experience made her question her priorities and feel defeated in the process. "But you know, without having the guidance you need like a class, and courses, and deadlines, and stuff is probably not a good fit either when you're managing so many things because then it becomes backburner."

P8 expected the faculty mentor to provide support and guidance with the dissertation process. P8 was also a faculty member at a different institution than the one that she was attending for her doctorate. She was looking for her faculty mentor to provide feedback on her research, the topic, and whether the topic had value.

P9 had very specific expectations for his faculty mentor since he was encouraged to come to this exact program to work with that mentor. At the start, P9 expected to work very closely with his faculty mentor on research projects; he also believed that he would be receiving financial assistance for his doctoral studies. "I expected to learn more about the research process. I've worked in public health, I've conducted research, so I didn't think I needed that much attention or handholding. However, I did expect to work closely together on research projects."

Information

Participants discussed the information they would like to know or information they might be missing because the doctoral process is not something, they knew much about. Participants expressed there was much about the process that they did not know and made statements like, "there is no manual on how to be a good PhD student." Participants mentioned the unspoken rules or norms they had to learn when they arrived at the institution. While sharing how she spoke directly with her dissertation committee members more than her faculty mentor, one participant stated, "I guess I also am a little bit wary about maybe just how the dynamics or maybe more from the political aspects of things." Participants discussed that they did not always know the process and procedure for getting their dissertation done or information about authorship, assistantships, grants, and how they had to learn along the way or as they made mistakes. Participants wanted their faculty mentors to help them "stay on track" with graduation and help them finish the degree on time. One participant stated that it is important for the faculty mentor to provide guidance and "[make] sure I am following along and progressing as I should be."

One participant had a different experience with information. P5 shared how his faculty mentor provided a great deal of information. P5 perceived his faculty mentor as someone who wanted him to succeed and provided him with information about process, procedure, and expectations to ensure that he would succeed. P5 shared a personal story about how he almost left the program because of some family issues, but his faculty mentor provided him with encouragement and shared her own personal story about the challenges she faced while pursuing her doctoral degree. P5 attributed her advice and encouragement to his decision to continue in the program. He shared how his faculty mentor consistently helped him, both academically and personally. "She would advise me on papers but most of the conversations that we had were about family and just life in general."

P8 shared that her faculty mentor was also involved in decision making about the doctoral process and shared much of what was happening at the planning level with his students. P8 described the mentor's sharing as "the inside scoop." However, P8 had to change faculty mentors because her mentor left the school. Her new faculty mentor was not as forthcoming with information or feedback on her dissertation.

Race

The code for "race" presented itself when participants were sharing about their experience as an African American student, the race of their faculty mentor, the race of their classmates, and their own race in connection to their faculty mentor, classmates, and or their dissertation topic. All participants self-identified as African American. Seven of the participants were assigned or selected dissertation mentors who were White. Two participants had African American faculty mentors. P1 shared her experiences with her academic advisor in comparison to her faculty mentor.

"I definitely think that my race has been a piece of my experience particularly because I did find an advisor who's Black; I felt like he is more invested in me and my advisor that wasn't (African American) didn't feel as invested in me, so from that standpoint I think it played a part."

P1 purposefully selected an African American faculty mentor, "I picked her because she actually seemed to have an interest in me and she was Black, too." Three of the participants, who did not have faculty mentors who were African American found African American faculty members in their departments who were able to provide them with unofficial mentoring.

P3, who had a White male faculty mentor, shared how her faculty mentor understood her and her research, "He…is a White man; I'm a Black woman. He understands…He really has a very unique and interesting perspective, in my opinion, on the work that we both do."

P5, a male participant, described his African American female faculty mentor as being "like a mom." He made this analogy based on how he perceived the support and encouragement she provided to him. When asked about the influence race has on persistence, P4 shared, "It could just be my perception or experience as being African American and knowing that sometimes you have to work harder." P4 shared that she based her belief on previous experiences. P5 shared his perception as a Black male in the doctoral program, "I've been the only Black male doctoral student in my department the whole time I've been here and I'm in my fourth year. There's never been another Black male since I've been here. There are post docs but not pre docs."

P8 was one of the participants who had a change in faculty mentors. Her first faculty mentor was a White male, but her second faculty mentor was a minority woman, not African American. P8 described that her experience between the two was completely different. P8 felt she had a better connection with the White male mentor. She felt supported by him. She did not feel that same support with the minority female mentor. P8 mentioned how the second mentor reacted to her topic, "she definitely had some issues with my topic being race related. She did not seem to want to discuss the issues or [did not seem] able to point me in the right direction." P8 sensed her mentor was uncomfortable in the conversations they had about race; the mentor also did not seem to understand the participant and was therefore slow to respond and provide feedback.

P9 was also a Black male student; his faculty mentor was a White male researcher. The participant, who was encouraged to leave his previous institution where he completed his master's degree in public health, shared his concern for his treatment compared to that of one of his classmates: "As a Black man, the only Black man in the program at the time, I do feel like there was some difference in treatment. The student that was working more closely with (faculty mentor name) is a White male. There was a difference once he arrived. It seemed like I was pushed to the side. I didn't understand them bringing me here only to have this happen. I could have stayed at the (other university name)."

P9 shared that he was offered a research assistantship but after the first year the award was cut in half. The reduction in award impacted his ability to be in school full-time and to meet his personal financial obligations. P9 had to take a job to make up for the financial loss. The second job was more time-consuming considering the travel time to and from the job and the expectations as a new employee along with his other responsibilities as a student and teaching assistant.

Diversity

Stemming from the discussion on race, participants mentioned diversity or lack of diversity within their institution, their department, school, or program. Most of the participants were the only African American students in the program, "I am the only Black person in my cohort." Participants shared what it was like to be the "only one" and their fear of living up to stereotypes, "One time we had a department retreat, and I was taking public transportation and I was really late, so I was the last person there. And I was like, 'oh, I'm going to be the late Black person,' like everyone is going to remember, but I think by now they forgot about it." (P2)

P3, who had the White male faculty mentor, shared her perception with respect to her research topic on race, "And it's been refreshing to have someone who doesn't look like me but is concerned about the violence among the people who look like me, to engage in conversation with and be frank; have frank conversations about the role of race in gun violence and a number of social and economic problems that we have in in urban America.

P8 described the overall institution as being diverse. However, the doctoral program where she was enrolled is not very diverse. P9 shared that the institution where he was enrolled lacks diversity. "It was not [diverse], there were mostly white women in the graduate program. Those faculty members who were able to advise doctoral students included only two White men. There was one Latina professor who did not teach much; she traveled quite a bit and focused her research on Latino/a health. There were two faculty of color teaching in the undergraduate and Master of Public Health programs, but not in the doctoral program.

Mental Health

Some emerging codes were not immediately noticed during the first review of the data. Participants mentioned issues related to mental health, feelings of isolation, anxiety, inadequacy, and self-doubt. Participants shared how "lonely" they felt in their programs. One participant stated that while she perceived her overall doctoral experience as positive, "I still feel like I'm out here by myself." Many of the participants mentioned how their faculty mentor was the only connection they had to the institution. Once students completed their courses and were no longer in the classroom with different faculty members and students, the dissertation process became more independent. P3 stated, "because so much of the doctoral program is self-guided, there have definitely been times where I've, many times, most times where I've felt unsure of myself."

Public Health Research Topics

Eight of the nine participants focused on public health topics and African Americans in their dissertation research. Some of the public health topics included: social determinants of health, men's health, urban violence, gun violence policy, cultural competency, health disparities, mental health, and colorectal cancer screening. P3 expressed that she was excited to work with her faculty mentor on her research and appreciated that her faculty mentor felt free to discuss racial issues related to her topic, no matter how uncomfortable. She stated how her faculty mentor supported her and encouraged her to do this research.

She said that he told her, "Most of the gun violence researchers are not Black which I still find astonishing, why are there not more Black people going into violence prevention research at least through public health but through criminology or it's just a dearth of Black people on the research side of violence prevention and he was very frank about that."

P2 expressed frustration with her faculty mentor not sharing the same enthusiasm for her dissertation research topic. P2 believed that her faculty mentor and dissertation committee were "not as invested in it because it's not their own work." Her faculty mentor was interested in social determinants of health, but focused on gender not race, which was P2's interest.

P5 focused on race, racism, and systemic structures in relation to urban violence. He grew up in the inner city near the university and felt that he needed to conduct research on the topic. P5 questioned if he was the only one (inner city Black male) in his school. He felt tremendous support from his faculty mentor who was Black and female. P5 appreciated the opportunity to do research addressing the problems in the inner city where he grew up and shared, "We already have the answer to these questions that we're asking; the problem is that it's not translating to the next level, to policy and interventions." P5 believed his presence at his school was "special." He also felt that the institution, located so close to the inner city, had a duty to provide research on the inner city.

"It's me holding this institution, as powerful as they are, accountable for that…they have to fulfill their obligation to 'the city' specifically if they want to be the world-renowned institution that they are, and they are, but to 'the city', they aren't.

CHAPTER 6

Faculty-Mentor Experiences

Faculty Experiences

Faculty support and assistance can be the starting point for success for students from minoritized backgrounds (Posselt, 2018). High quality mentorship can provide insight into academic norms as well as concepts and ideas from the field that students would not learn on their own: the unwritten norms and expectations. Some faculty shared their experiences engaging with Black doctoral students, including successes and challenges and their perspective on how they provide (and students receive) support. Dr. Brenda Seals shared her experiences based on her work with doctoral students at two different universities:

"Listening seems to be a key feature. I try to find out what drives their passions. My approach is to try to support whatever they want to do, albeit, tempered with my experience of the possibilities. Second is believing in them with unrivaled support—seeing their talents and focusing there. I make sure to let them know how excited I am about their potential AND where they are now. I find that being proud is contagious. Third, I do try to challenge them, to encourage thinking beyond their current project. Yes, I give too much feedback but that allows me to see how they think and what directions they can go. From my first doctoral student at Tulane University in the

1990s, I also try to always stay in touch. She ultimately became a professor at Howard University and "semi-retired" to practice mental health. Perhaps it is cliche to "pay it forward" but I am always amazed when I catch up with former students to see all of the wonderful things they do and their long "to do" list. Way beyond a "bucket list", these students have always faced an uphill battle and their motivation does not lag. A distinct challenge was seeing racism in action. One of my first students at Tulane University kept being held back in her written exams from the other oral exam graders. The other graders said her "writing" was not good. So, I copied and made anonymous a few examples and asked another professor in rhetoric to "grade" the language. As I thought, the student in question ranked among the top writers. My suspicions were confirmed when a really weak Caucasian student passed the oral exams on her first try and my student didn't make the committee cut on her second try.

Ultimately, she left Tulane and got her doctorate at a different institution--more prestigious than Tulane. Another notable challenge is what I see as "self-destruction." When some students get towards the end, they seem to struggle anew in the "light at the end of the tunnel." I'm not sure how to help these students, but not giving up is key. Their doctoral work may not be as timely as some others, but once they finish, they skyrocket with pent up energy. Fireworks!"

Dr. Rachel Hardman from the Center for Antiracism Research for Health Equity at the University of Minnesota School of Public Health shares more about the unspoken norms and expectations otherwise known as the hidden curriculum (Ampaw & Jaeger, 2012). *"Mentoring and engaging Black doctoral students in my research as well as helping them with the socialization process in the world of academia is critically important to my personal and professional mission. Overall, I endeavor to be the mentor that I never had. I endeavor to be the person who helps students navigate the hidden curriculum and hidden institutional norms. I strive to listen and tell them they are indeed not crazy and that their feelings are valid when a colleague or faculty member says or does something racist. The most important strategy in my work to engage Black doctoral students is to build community (social and intellectual). I have brought together Black doctoral students from across the country who are all focused on the measurement of structural racism. We convene virtually once a month to discuss our research, professional development, to vent and to build on our futures."*

While racially minoritized doctoral students have benefited from mentorship from faculty of different racial backgrounds, the mentorship from faculty from the same background has proven to be even more beneficial (Blockett et al, 2016). Representation is significant. Having access to tenured faculty who have the same background and sometimes similar stories, learning from them, and garnering their support are crucial to the doctoral experience for these students. It has also been shown to be beneficial for the faculty providing support and mentorship as shared here by Dr. Lisa Bowleg of George Washington University: "*Well, I'm deeply committed to mentoring doctoral students and so one of the first things that I do is actively recruit doctoral students such as two of my three current students. Thereafter, I try to get a sense of where my students want to go and learn their strengths and weaknesses. I invite them to collaborate on grant proposals and publications, incorporate them as core members of my research team and ensure that they are exposed to all aspects of the research process and what it means to be a faculty member in the academy. We talk not just about their work for my team and schoolwork, but also about their personal lives and struggles, particularly as Black people in predominantly White institutions. I try and teach, using my own experiences as a Black woman in the academy, but also try and be a support system for the inevitable microaggressions and other hassles they have to field.*"

Faculty mentors provide guidance and support so that students can navigate the academic spaces with confidence. As demonstrated here by Dr. Delores James of University of Florida:

The basic philosophy that I instill is that 'you have the power to change the world.' And, one of the ways that you do that is to be a generator of knowledge rather than being a mere consumer. Thus, it is important to be a great writer and to find ways to master your writing skills. Writing can be intimidating, but you get better the more you do it. I also help students to work through the 'impostor syndrome.' You have to believe that you belong here, especially if you're at a predominantly white institution. Start by showing up to as many events as possible. Introduce yourself to the Chair as well as every faculty in the department (even if you never take their classes). You can take it to the next level by introducing yourself to the Associate Dean for Academic Affairs as well as the Dean. Offer to meet them for coffee. The goal here is to add advocates as well as mentors to your circle of influence. Embrace failure and all the lessons that it brings.

CHAPTER 7

The Public Health Approach

Having low percentages of public health doctoral students recruited, retained, and graduated while also having a low percentage of public health faculty is a public health problem. We do a disservice to the field by letting this problem continue considering how significantly it impacts the work that we do. The Healthy People 2030 goals are contingent upon the training and education of the public health workforce and that training and education is contingent upon those doing the training and educating. While there are some professionals working in public health who do not have degrees in public health, most of the workforce is degreed at the bachelor’s or master's level from schools or programs of public health.

Just like any other public health problem, I propose we take a public health approach to solving this problem. "The public health approach involves defining and measuring the problem, determining the cause or risk factors for the problem, determining how to prevent or ameliorate the problem, and implementing effective strategies on a larger scale and evaluating the impact."

I invite institutional leaders to reflect on the policies and practices at your institution to ensure that those policies and practices are not creating barriers and challenges to Black students.

When I say reflect, I don't mean reading or glancing over them. This may require a deep dive. This may require engaging experts, faculty, and students and asking tough questions. This exercise may reveal some ugly truths. Be prepared to be uncomfortable. Your quest for recognition, awards, and funding may come at the expense of continuing racist practices. That's one of the reasons anti-racism is so hard, racism has benefits. It's time to be honest about how we benefit from racism. The racism we see is so ugly— angry, hateful people harassing a Black child as she walks into a newly desegregated school or a Black man, a bird watcher, being berated by a White woman in a park (ABC7, 2020). The racism we see is merely a symptom of systemic racism – institutional racism. The racism we see is easy to point to it and be outraged. It is easy to condemn. We can name legislation after it like the CAREN Act.

We can produce television shows and movies about it. We do this all while continuing to function within systems built on racist ideology. With these policies securely in place, they can be carried out year after year regardless of who is in leadership until they are changed. Even when a Black person becomes a university president their abilities will be limited by these policies. That president may even be harmed by them— *correction*— that president will be harmed by them because they will function as they were intended. This is the problem. We've been monitoring it for years, we have enough evidence of its existence and its ability to negatively impact our students, faculty and staff. Once we can admit it and own it, only then can we start the process of addressing it. This may be the most challenging part for many institutions. However, for those who are ready, let's get to work.

We have identified the problem, its cause and the risk factors. The next step in the public health approach is to determine how to prevent or ameliorate the problem, develop effective strategies, and then evaluate for impact. One thing institutions do a great job of is collecting data. This data can be used to understand the ways in which institutions recruit, retain, and graduate students in a different way than what has been previously practiced. In reviewing policies and practices, a mind shift is needed— challenging your way of thinking.

In public health, we have a keen understanding of how difficult it can be to change behavior. We have developed theories and frameworks that help us determine how to go about developing interventions to assist in changing behaviors. We could use any one of these to assist in the behavior change necessary to shift to an anti-racist mindset and in turn anti-racist practices.

For example, the *Health Belief Model* (Sharma, 2022) focuses on perception and how perception can lead to action or inaction. If you don't perceive it to be a problem, or that you are at risk, then you are the least likely to change your behavior. The *Transtheoretical Model* for change allows you to move between stages, starting with the precontemplation stage as you are building your awareness about your need for change (Sharma, 2022). There's no time frame for each stage and you can move back and forth as needed. We can apply any one of these theories in our quest to build equitable and inclusive higher education institutions. If the institutions are not ready for change, the school and program leaders may need to do this work on their own. Ideally the change should happen institution wide but if that is not possible, we can take the harm reduction approach and do what is in our power to do with the resources we have available.

CHAPTER 8

Diversity, Equity, Inclusion and Belonging

In June 2020, after the murder of George Floyd, like some corporations and politicians, many higher education institutions released official statements in solidarity expressing support for Black or Black Indigenous People of Color (BIPOC) students, faculty, and staff. There were statements that stated very clearly that they condemned racism but there were also statements sharing how George Floyd "died in police custody," instead of stating that he was murdered. Quite a few higher education institutions released these statements while also having active civil rights cases against them. These statements were followed by the introduction of new programs and departments focused on diversity, equity, and inclusion. Some that already had these resources in place increased funding and staff support. There were forums and protests. There were numerous virtual forums and webinars highlighting topics like microaggressions, pay equality, decolonizing syllabi, and allyship. Much of this work to enlighten others about racism and its outcomes were left to Black faculty and staff who were already dealing with the emotional toll of the racial and social justice events in the nation and in their communities.

Many Black students, faculty, and staff took to social media to raise awareness about the racism that has been happening in the form of Instagram pages named "Black at _______", describing what it's like to be Black at a particular school. The posts are anonymous. People who want to share, send their post to the page administrator. On Twitter, there are hashtags like

#Blackintheivory for Black faculty and staff who share about their experiences with racism on their campuses. These tweets are not anonymous; people tweet directly from their Twitter accounts. I would ask my non-Black colleagues if they knew about the pages, many responding that they didn't know and were quite surprised. Some only had Facebook pages or no social media at all, which is unfortunate because many could benefit from learning more about the experiences of their students and fellow faculty members. One post from a "Black at _______" Instagram page states: "Being a Black woman in a doctoral program is exhausting. The advisors do not view you as a priority and if you have concerns about why you haven't made significant progress with your research, then you are viewed as the problem. It's no secret that the majority of funding and TA opportunities are given to White female grad students over more qualified Black graduate students, especially WOC…" (Black at Temple, 2020). Fill in the blank with your school and see what has been shared.

Black in the Ivory has grown from a hashtag to a Twitter page to a book. It's a movement. The Twitter page bio states that the purpose is to "amplify the voices of 'Blackademics', to speak truth about racism in academia." (Black in the Ivory Twitter Page, 2021). An example of a tweet with the hashtag #BlackintheIvory is from an Assistant Professor, "Sitting here wondering how I'm supposed to interpret 'wanting me to be successful' in the face of continued inequitable workloads, expectations and accommodations… #burnout is real…" (Richard, 2021).

While social supports are being created for those who have experienced racism in various education institutions, most recently, we have parents in an uproar over the possibility of their children being taught about critical race theory (CRT). The discussion around CRT is focused on political parties and indoctrinating children by teaching them about the nation's history. The use of CRT in certain conversations makes it blatantly obvious that its origin and purpose are not widely known or understood. School board meetings across the country are now having discussions about whether or not CRT should be taught in schools. North Carolina just passed legislation in both houses that would control how students and teachers discuss race in the classroom. (House Bill 324, 2021)

Talking about racism is uncomfortable for some. James Baldwin stated that, "Not everything that is faced can be changed. But nothing can be changed until it is faced" (Baldwin, 1962). Continuing to ignore it, deny it, and make excuses for it only makes the problem worse.

Have courageous conversations, then move to action. Proactive anti-racism is required. It's important to move beyond reactionary activism, waiting until an injustice goes viral before doing something about it. That keeps us in continual crisis mode which is not healthy. We have to work together to meet the needs of BIPOC students. Combating systemic racism requires effort and actual changes to the student experience. Faculty play a role, but faculty can only do what institutions enable and empower them to do.

CHAPTER 9

What's Next? (The Ideal Outcomes)

In an ideal world, institutional leaders would recognize this problem and convene a working group or task force to come up with a plan on how to dismantle systemic racism at their institutions. They would draft an extensive literature review on best practices. Those that can afford it would hire a consulting firm or consultants who specialize in developing and implementing anti-racist policies and procedures. They would go line by line reviewing all institutional policy documents. They would develop and disseminate surveys to all stakeholders. Using the findings to develop a strategy that includes clear goals, S.M.A.R.T. goals. They would make it known that this effort is underway--enlisting the support of partners, collaborators, and community. This is an "all hands-on deck" situation.

Since we do not live in an ideal world, our reality consists of many facets that will not only come against such an effort, but blatantly sabotage it. Any institution that engages in the efforts I describe above will face challenges detrimental to its existence. With many institutions balancing student interests with parent interests and donor interests and research funder interests and the list goes on — embarking on this journey would be extremely controversial.

In the interest of focusing on more realistic efforts, let us take a look at what can be done by schools and programs, faculty, and staff. Individual schools and programs can take the steps stated above, but on a smaller scale. Bringing on a permanent position for one who specializes in anti-racist policy change would be the best decision. Cutting corners and using people who are not trained in this area would be a wasted effort and could do more harm than good. Not everyone doing DEI work is doing anti-racist work. They are not one in the same. Start there.

While doing the work above, let's examine our recruitment and hiring practices. Let's institutionalize purposeful recruitment practices. Merely posting a job description to Higher Ed Jobs or INDEED is far from purposeful. That is the bare minimum. Utilize social media, go to graduate schools, their alumni pool — *all graduate schools*, including Historically Black Colleges and Universities. The talent is there. Be transparent about pay, benefits, and opportunities.

We want to get away from 'Mikes hiring other Mikes.' (Forbes, 2018). Let's train our hiring managers and hiring committee members to view candidates from a lens free from bias. The research shows that those in the position to hire faculty are making the decision based on their own personal ideas, assumptions, needs, and comfort. We can create 100 DEI positions and departments, but we will never achieve its goals until we address how we recruit and hire talent.

What's Next? (The Ideal Outcomes)

The next issue to address is retainment. Once you have diverse talent, will they thrive at your institution? How can you make sure they thrive? Talented people shine. Are there any practices, policies, or people who will block that shine? Many Black and Brown faculty and staff leave institutions or the academy as a whole because they have been used, abused, and devalued. Faculty and staff from diverse backgrounds challenge the status quo merely by being present.

Their presence should be welcomed but instead, often it is resented. From verbal disrespect to undermining behavior and sabotage to microaggressions. The experience is truly toxic. You know the phrase, "go where you are celebrated?" Many have decided to do just that.

For faculty, it is your responsibility to seek out education and training opportunities that will enhance your ability to be anti-racist in your teaching, advising, mentoring, and co-existing as colleagues to your fellow coworkers. I have included resources at the end of this book. A change in mindset, new understanding, and empathy are what's needed. Take the time to reflect on your own thoughts and behaviors. Get uncomfortable.

Afterword: Final Reflections

A Call to Action

I have taught at six higher education institutions over the last 16 years. Some private, some public —as adjunct faculty, non-tenure track faculty, and tenure track faculty. While each institution had its own characteristics, I had the same experience once on campus: students who identified as African, African American, Black, Dominican, and Puerto Rican would make their way to my office to introduce themselves. Some would say that they "heard about" there was a new professor who was Black, while others would only say that they were glad to meet me.

Students who had children also gravitated to my office, asking about the pictures of my son on my desk. In our discussions they would learn that I had my son during my sophomore year of college. They would also learn that I was the first in my family to obtain a bachelor's, master's and eventually a doctoral degree in my family. My life experiences and my identity were similar to theirs and we connected. I would see them in class or advising meetings and others would formally ask me to be their mentor. I would always say yes. Of course, this speaks to increased "invisible labor" for many Black faculty, which has many implications for non-tenure and tenure track faculty (Flaherty, 2020). It was time consuming, but I felt that it was necessary to provide guidance — to share with them many of the unspoken, unwritten rules, and expectations in higher education:

the hidden curriculum. Much of what I shared with them were things I had to learn on my own and they did not have access to this information otherwise.

A conversation with one of my students constantly plays in my head. We discussed her career goals and her academic goals, and when discussing her classes, she asked me, "Why did it take so long for me to have a professor who looks like me?" That question stopped me in my tracks. She was genuine in her quest to understand why she had been at this school, taking many classes, and it was not until her junior year that she would have a Black professor. There was sadness and frustration in her voice. She expressed how comfortable she felt speaking with me and how it seemed like I understood her world because I shared similar experiences. I also understood that this question was not about me personally. This was not a compliment to my mentorship. This question that she asked laid bare the systemic problem that most higher education institutions face.

I am hopeful that this book provides the foundational knowledge necessary for faculty, not just in public health, and institutions to think about how to improve and raise awareness about this problem. Each chapter could be its own book. Sustainability is necessary and that will take more work, more understanding, and more accountability. Black faculty, Black women faculty, and women in general are leaving academia to go into industry or become entrepreneurs because of treatment and the strain on their mental health. The students will lose out because of this. Colleges are scrambling to figure out how to create more sustainable revenue streams while also trying to address the lack of diversity in students and faculty. Recruiting and retaining students and faculty from diverse backgrounds is the answer to the financial sustainability problem but this work cannot just be about money. As soon as there are genuine and systemic changes that focuses on justice, equity, diversity, inclusion and belonging, only then will there be the financial return on the investment. Institutional racism is costly. It costs time, effort, and money. It's time to do the work to combat institutional racism. Are you ready?

References

ABC7 (2020, June 9). *Central Park: White woman ID'ed as Amy Cooper in NYC calls police on black man over dog leash* [Video]. Youtube. https://youtu.be/9TXkh9jihUU

Aburto, J. M., Kristensen, F. F., & Sharp, P. (2020). Black-White disparities during an epidemic: Life expectancy and lifespan disparity in the US, 1980-2000. *Economics & Human Biology*, 100937. https://doi.org/10.1016/j.ehb.2020.100937

American School Counselor Association (2019). The ASCA national model: A framework for school counseling programs (4th ed.). Alexandria, VA: Author.

Archer-Banks, D. A. M., & Behar-Horenstein, L. S. (2011). Ogbu revisited. *Urban Education*, *47*(1), 198–223. https://doi.org/10.1177/0042085911427739

Baldwin, J. (1962). As much truth as one can bear [essay]. New York Times Book Review. Retrieved from https://www.nytimes.com/1962/01/14/archives/as-much-truth-as-one-can-bear-to-speak-out-about-the-world-as-it-is.html

Behar-Horenstein, L., & Zhang, H. (2018). From contemplation to action: Mechanisms of change in the mentoring academy. *The Qualitative Report*. https://doi.org/10.46743/2160-3715/2018.3376

Bester, N., & Milan, N. (2022, February 2). *A War on Marijuana, or a War on Black Communities?* ACLU of Maryland. https://www.aclu-md.org/en/news/war-marijuana-or-war-black-communities

Black at Temple [@blackattemple]. (2020, July 23). Being a Black Woman in Temple's Doctoral Program is Exhausting [photograph]. Retrieved from https://www.instagram.com/p/CC_m9Lknulv/?igshid=ZjA0NjI3M2I=

Blockett, R. A., Felder, P. P., Parrish, W., III, & Collier, J. (2016). *Pathways to the professoriate: Exploring Black doctoral student socialization and the pipeline to the academic profession.* Scholar.google.com. https://scholar.google.com/citations?view_op=view_citation&hl=en&user=K9q1Y-oAAAAJ&citation_for_view=K9q1Y-oAAAAJ:u-x6o8ySG0sC

Bruce Duncan Perry, & Oprah Winfrey. (2021). *What happened to you? : Conversations on trauma, resilience, and healing.* Flatiron Books.

Buchanan, R. J., & Hatcher, W. (2007). Compassionate Conservatism: Federal Funding for the Ryan White CARE Act During the Bush Administration. *American Journal of Public Health, 97*(11), 2013–2016. https://doi.org/10.2105/ajph.2006.107573

Refrences

Couture, V. G., & Bang, N. M. (2022). LGBTQ Students in Higher Education. *Handbook of Research on Opening Pathways for Marginalized Individuals in Higher Education*, 171–191. https://doi.org/10.4018/978-1-6684-3819-0.ch010

Doughty, K. (2020). Increasing trauma-informed awareness and practice in higher education. *Journal of Continuing Education in the Health Professions*, *40*(1), 66–68. https://doi.org/10.1097/ceh.0000000000000279

Felder, P. (2010). On doctoral student development: Exploring faculty mentoring in the shaping of African American doctoral student success. *The Qualitative Report.* https://www.semanticscholar.org/paper/On-Doctoral-Student-Development%3A-Exploring-Faculty-Felder/4be82c36491d2742696696eccaeb73748c14a966

Felder, P., Stevenson, H., & Gasman, M. (2014). Why you mistakenly hire people just like you. *International Journal of Doctoral Studies*, *9*, 21–42. http://ijds.org/Volume9/IJDSv9p021-042Felder0323.pdf

Fernandez-Pena, J. R. (2021, October 24). President Welcome Address [speech audio recording]

APHA https://apha.confex.com/apha/2021/meetingapp.cgi/Session/64174

Gildersleeve, R. E., Croom, N. N., & Vasquez, P. L. (2011). "Am I going crazy?!": A critical race analysis of doctoral education. *Equity & Excellence in Education, 44*(1), 93–114. https://doi.org/10.1080/10665684.2011.539472

Herr-Perrin, A. (2021, December 22). *JEDI is trending in higher education. but hbcus have modeled it all along.* Diverse Issues in Higher Education. https://www.diverseeducation.com/opinion/article/15286615/jedi-is-trending-in-higher-education-but-hbcus-have-modeled-it-all-along

Johnson, J. L., Spivey, C. A., & Chisholm-Burns, M. A. (2021). Comparison of Black student enrollment in colleges of pharmacy, medicine, and dentistry. *American Journal of Pharmaceutical Education*, 8493. https://doi.org/10.5688/ajpe8493

Jones, Y. A. (2019). "I was the only one in the building." lived experiences of Black school counselors post-"Brown v. board of education" in predominantly white schools. In *ERIC*. ProQuest LLC. https://eric.ed.gov/?id=ED604876

Manoj Sharma. (2022). *Theoretical foundations of health education and health promotion*. Jones & Bartlett Learning.

Matthew, P. A. (2016, November 23). *What Is faculty diversity worth to a university?* The Atlantic. https://www.theatlantic.com/education/archive/2016/11/what-is-faculty-diversity-worth-to-a-university/508334/

Mayes, R. D., Lowery, K., Mims, L. C., & Rodman, J. (2021). "I stayed just above the cusp so I was left alone": Black girls' experiences with school counselors. *The High School Journal*, *104*(3), 131–154. https://doi.org/10.1353/hsj.2021.0003

Mitchell, L. D., Parlamis, J. D., & Claiborne, S. A. (2014). Overcoming faculty avoidance of online education. *Journal of Management Education*, *39*(3), 350–371. https://doi.org/10.1177/1052562914547964

National Center for Education Statistics. (2017a). *Fast facts: Historically Black colleges and universities*. Ed.gov; National Center for Education Statistics. https://nces.ed.gov/fastfacts/display.asp?id=667

National Center for Education Statistics. (2017b). *Percentage of degree-granting postsecondary institutions with a tenure system and percentage of full-time faculty with tenure at these institutions, by control and level of institution and selected characteristics of faculty: Selected years, 1993-94 through 2018-19.* Ed.gov; National Center for Education Statistics. https://nces.ed.gov/programs/digest/d19/tables/dt19_316.80.asp

Nelson, Y. M. (2019). Strategies for mentoring diverse students. *Nurse Educator*, *44*(3), 146. https://doi.org/10.1097/nne.0000000000000631

Oglesby, A., & Drake, R. (2020). Humanity is not a thing: Disrupting white supremacy in K-12 social emotional learning. *Journal of Critical Thought and Praxis*. https://doi.org/10.31274/jctp.11549

Patterson, N. A. (2020). *Mentoring Experiences of African American Doctoral Students in Public Health: A Qualitative Study* (Doctoral dissertation, Capella University).

Perez, R. J., Harris, Jr, L. W., Robbins, C. K., & Montgomery, C. (2019). Graduate students' agency and resistance after oppressive experiences. *Studies in Graduate and Postdoctoral Education*, *11*(1), 57–71. https://doi.org/10.1108/sgpe-06-2019-0057

Posselt, J. (2018). Normalizing struggle: Dimensions of faculty support for doctoral students and implications for persistence and well-being. *The Journal of Higher Education*, *89*(6), 988–1013. https://doi.org/10.1080/00221546.2018.1449080

Press, M. R. S., The Associated Press, Kathy Young, The Associated. (2020, November 17). *Public health programs see surge in students amid pandemic*. Kaiser Health News. https://khn.org/news/public-health-degree-programs-see-surge-in-students-amid-pandemic/

Ranji, U., Jul 15, I. G. P., & 2022. (2022, July 15). *What are the implications of the overturning of Roe v. Wade for racial disparities?* KFF. https://www.kff.org/racial-equity-and-health-policy/issue-brief/what-are-the-implications-of-the-overturning-of-roe-v-wade-for-racial-disparities/

Smith, M.R. & Young, K. (2020). Public health programs see surge in students amid pandemic. Kaiser Health News. Retrieved from https://khn.org/news/public-health-degree-programs-see-surge-in-students-amid-pandemic/

Stanton, J. D., Means, D. R., Babatola, O., Osondu, C., Oni, O., & Mekonnen, B. (2022). Drawing on internal strengths and creating spaces for growth: How black science majors navigate the racial climate at a predominantly white institution to succeed. *CBE—Life Sciences Education, 21*(1). https://doi.org/10.1187/cbe.21-02-0049

Truong, K., & Museus, S. (2012). Responding to racism and racial trauma in doctoral study: An inventory for coping and mediating relationships. *Harvard Educational Review, 82*(2), 226–254. https://doi.org/10.17763/haer.82.2.u54154j787323302

Van Der Kolk, B. (2014). *The body keeps the score: Brain, mind, and body in the healing of trauma.* Penguin Books.

Van Schyndel, J. L., Koontz, S., McPherson, S., Reese, C., Sarginson, D. R., Scoggins, L., Woods, R. A., & Wendler, M. C. (2019). Faculty Support for a Culture of Scholarship of Discovery: A Literature Review. *Journal of Professional Nursing, 35*(6), 480–490. https://doi.org/10.1016/j.profnurs.2019.05.001

Yost, J., Dobbins, M., Traynor, R., DeCorby, K., Workentine, S., & Greco, L. (2014). Tools to support evidence-informed public health decision making. *BMC Public Health*, *14*(1). https://doi.org/10.1186/1471-2458-14-728

Glossary

Definitions

Anti-Racism: "the policy or practice of opposing racism and promoting racial tolerance that leads to racial equity and is substantiated by anti-racist ideas" (Kendi, 2019).

BIPOC: an acronym that stands for Black Indigenous People of Color

Institutional Racism: "can be defined as an infrastructure of rulings, ordinances or statutes promulgated by a sovereign government or authoritative entity, whereas such ordinances and statutes entitle one ethnic group in a society certain rights and privileges, while denying other groups in that society these same rights and privileges because of long-established cultural prejudices, religious prejudices, fears, myths, and Xenophobia held by the entitled group" (United Nations Human Rights, 2021).

Marginalized: "relegated to an unimportant or powerless position within a society or group" (Merriam-Webster, 2021).

Mentoring: "the act of providing guidance and support delivered from a mentor to a protegé. (Thomas, Willis, & Davis, 2007).

S.M.A.R.T.: Specific, Measurable, Achievable, Relevant, Time-bound

Systemic Racism: "can be defined as the racial attitudes found in a ethnic group's traditions, beliefs, opinions, and myths that are firmly ingrained in the very fiber of the ethnic group's cultural paradigm, where such traditions, beliefs, opinions, and myths have been practiced and sustained for so long, that they are accepted as common facts, understood to be normal behavioral practices whereas, such practices in effect marginalize, and demonize the human worth of another ethnic group" (United Nations Human Rights, 2021).

Resource Guide

Anti-Racism Initiatives in Higher Education

Anti-Racist Pedagogy in Higher Education at Merrimack College
https://libguides.merrimack.edu/antiracism/HE

Boston University Center for Anti-racist Research
https://www.bu.edu/antiracism-center/

New York University (NYU) Anti-Racism Education, Programs and Resources https://www.nyu.edu/life/global-inclusion-and-diversity/anti-racism.html

Stanford University Black Community Service Center
https://bcsc.stanford.edu/

Tulane University School of Public Health Anti-Racism academic resources https://sph.tulane.edu/antiracism

University of Florida Anti-Racism resources and activities
https://antiracism.ufl.edu/

Mentoring Programs

McMaster University Black Student Mentorship Program https://blackstudentsuccess.mcmaster.ca/the-black-student-mentorship-program-bsmp/

The PhD Project https://phdproject.org/

The University Centers for Exemplary Mentoring (UCEM) https://sloan.org/programs/higher-education/diversity-equity-inclusion/minority-phd-program

University of California Santa Barbara Black Student Engagement Program https://academics.sa.ucsb.edu/programs/black-resource-committee/bsep

Moving Forward Together Initiatives LLC https://movingforwardtogetherinitiativesllc.com/

Readings

"Am I Going Crazy? A Critical Race Analysis of Doctoral Education" https://www.tandfonline.com/doi/abs/10.1080/10665684.2011.539472

Resource Guide

"Graduate students' agency and resistance after oppressive experiences" https://www.emerald.com/insight/content/doi/10.1108/SGPE-06-2019-0057/full/html

Nelson. (2019). Strategies for Mentoring Diverse Students. Nurse Educator, 44(3), 146–146. https://doi.org/10.1097/NNE.0000000000000631

Truong, K. A., & Museus, S. D. (2012). Responding to racism and racial trauma in doctoral study: An inventory for coping and mediating relationships. Harvard Educational Review, 82 (2), 226-254.

Van der Kolk, B.A. (2015). The body keeps score: Brain, mind, and body in the healing of trauma. Penguin Books.

About the Author

Natasha A. Patterson, PhD, MPH

Dr. Natasha Patterson is currently a Professor of Public Health at The College of New Jersey (TCNJ) in Ewing, NJ, teaching leadership, health education, and health policy courses for undergraduate and graduate students. Dr. Patterson has been teaching in higher education for over 15 years. Prior to teaching she worked in the field as a Health Educator, Program Coordinator for a community-based organization and a Research Program Manager for world renowned cancer research center. Her current research interests include social justice and health disparities, and student engagement and success.

Dr. Patterson presents at international, national and local conferences and sits on expert panels, most recently she was a panelist for National Public Health Week speaking on Public Health Careers for Arcadia University. Dr. Patterson mentors' high school and college students as well as professionals in or transitional to public health and higher education positions. She provides the information and support they need to reach their academic and career goals. She extends this work into her civic and community engagement as a member of the National Coalition of 100 Black Women, Inc. PA Chapter, the National Association of University Women Suburban Philadelphia Branch, and serving on the boards of Temple University Black Alumni Alliance and HealthSpark Foundation.

Dr. Patterson is the Founder and CEO of On the Journey to Better, LLC, a specialized consulting firm created to provide services and solutions that will enable individuals and organizations in the higher education space to improve in various ways. Services include: preparing individuals for careers in higher education and public health; educating and empowering individuals and institutions to improve in their diversity, equity and inclusive; and assisting higher education institutions who are serious about reducing and repairing the harms inflicted on faculty, staff, and students from traditionally excluded populations: This can only be done through systems change: changes to the polices, practices, and culture of the institution.